Networks

Second Edition

F R Connor

Ph D, M Sc, B Sc (Eng) Hons, ACGI,
C Eng, MIEE, MIERE, M Inst P

Edward Arnold

First published in Great Britain 1972 by
Edward Arnold (Publishers) Ltd, 41 Bedford Square, London WC1B 3DQ
Edward Arnold, 3 East Read Street, Baltimore, Maryland 21202, U.S.A.
Edward Arnold (Australia) Pty Ltd, 80 Waverley Road, Caulfield East,
Victoria 3145, Australia

Reprinted 1975, 1978, 1979, 1980, 1984
Second Edition 1986

British Library Cataloguing in Publication Data

Connor, F. R.
   Networks.—2nd ed.
   1. Telecommunication systems
   I. Title
   621.38   TK5101

   ISBN 0-7131-3577-8

Text set in 10/11 Times Monophoto
by Macmillan India Ltd, Bangalore 25
Printed and bound in Great Britain by
Whitstable Litho Ltd, Kent

Preface

In this new edition, certain parts of the text have been revised and extended. Chapter 2 on one-port networks includes a section on *RC* and *RL* networks, while Chapter 3 on two-port networks has been extended to include the twin-T network and various details on network parameters. Modern filter theory in Chapter 4 contains a section on elliptic function filters while Chapter 5 on active filters has been extended to cover operational amplifiers and various filter realizations. Chapter 6 is now devoted entirely to the important subject of digital filters which are used in many practical applications. As in the earlier edition, worked examples are provided in the text, together with a set of problems and answers. A list of many useful references is also included for the interested reader together with various Appendices to cover details on CCD and SAW filters, prototype filters, operational amplifiers and filter tables.

The aim of the book is the same as in the first edition though it should be pointed out that Higher National Certificates and Higher National Diplomas are now awarded by the Business and Technician Education Council. Furthermore, the Council of Engineering Institutions examination is now the responsibility of the Engineering Council and is called the Engineering Council examination.

In conclusion, the author would like to express his sincere thanks to those of his readers who so kindly sent in some corrections for the earlier edition.

1986   FRC

Preface to the first edition

This is an introductory book on the important topic of Networks. Such networks are used extensively in the fields of Electronics and Telecommunications, and the book endeavours to present the basic ideas in a concise and coherent manner. Moreover, to assist in the assimilation of these basic ideas, many worked examples from past examination papers have been provided to illustrate clearly the application of the fundamental theory.

The first part of the book is devoted to an analysis of the various types of one-port and two-port networks, emphasis being placed on their particular characteristics. Subsequent chapters then deal specifically with the important class of networks known as filters and consideration is given to the practical problem of their design. Finally, the book ends with a chapter on the more modern approach of synthesis, which is applied to the field of filter design, thereby presenting a unified and broad outline of this extremely useful topic.

The book will be found useful by students preparing for London University examinations, degrees of the Council of National Academic Awards, examinations of the Council of Engineering Institutions and for other qualifications such as Higher National Certificates, Higher National Diploma and certain examinations of the City & Guilds of London Institute. It will also be useful to practising engineers in industry who require a ready source of basic knowledge to help them in their applied work.

1972   FRC

Acknowledgements

The author wishes to thank the Senate of the University of London and the Council of the Institution of Electrical Engineers, for permission to include questions from their past examination papers. The solutions provided are his own and he accepts full responsibility for them.

Finally, the author would like to thank the publishers for various useful suggestions and will be grateful to his readers for drawing his attention to any errors which may have occurred.

Abbreviations

C.E.I.   Council of Engineering Institutions examination, Part 2.
U.L.   University of London, BSc (Eng) examination in Telecommunication, Part 3.

Contents

Symbols

a	any constant
	incident wave
b	any constant
	scattered wave
f_r	resonant frequency
f_s	sampling frequency
	s-plane frequency
f_z	z-plane frequency
g	g parameter
g_i	gain parameter
h	h parameter
$h(n)$	impulse response
$h_T(n)$	truncated value of $h(n)$
i	current
k	any factor
m	any number
n	any number
	nth order
p_j	jth pole
s	complex variable
	s parameter
s_n	normalised value of s
v	voltage
$w(n)$	window function
$x(n)$	series of n sampled values
y	y parameter
z	the quantity e^{sT}
	z parameter
z_i	ith zero
A	any parameter
	voltage gain
A_c	closed-loop gain
A_o	open-loop gain
B	any parameter
C	any parameter
$C_n(\omega)$	Chebyshev polynomial
D	any parameter
G	gyration resistance
H	scale factor
$H(s)$	transfer function (s-plane)
$H(z)$	transfer function (z-plane)
I	current
K	op amp gain

L	inductance
N	any number
P	power
Q	Q-factor
R	resistance
R_f	feedback resistance
$R_n(\omega)$	Chebyshev rational function
R_0	characteristic resistance
S	sensitivity factor
T	sampling period
V	voltage
$W(f)$	Fourier transform of $w(n)$
X	reactance
$X(z)$	z-transform of $x(n)$
Y	admittance
$Y(s)$	driving-point admittance
Z	impedance
Z_d	dynamic impedance
Z_i	input impedance
Z_L	load impedance
Z_0	characteristic impedance
$Z(s)$	driving-point impedance
α	attenuation coefficient
	the quantity $(\delta f / f_r)$
β	phase-change coefficient
	feedback factor
γ	propagation coefficient
ε	any number
θ	angle
	image transfer coefficient
σ	the real part of s
ω	angular frequency
ω_c	angular cut-off frequency
ω_0	angular resonant frequency

1
Introduction

Networks are used extensively in telecommunication circuits and form the basic structure of the transmission line or composite filter.

At present, the most widely used network is the *passive* network which has no internal voltages. A passive network is therefore an arrangement of components such as resistors, inductors or capacitors in the form of a physical structure; various types of structure are possible, each having its own particular properties and applications.

However, more recently, *active* networks that contain devices such as transistors, are being used more often, as they possess some useful advantages over the usual passive networks.

1.1   Passive networks

The two most basic structures are the one-port network and the two-port network shown in Fig. 1.1. A one-port network has a pair of terminals only, while a two-port network has two input terminals and two output terminals.

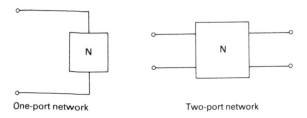

One-port network   Two-port network

Fig. 1.1

It is common practice to regard the network as a 'black-box' to which the appropriate terminals are attached and an analysis is made on this basic 'black-box' configuration.

1.2   Examples of networks

Typical networks used in communication systems are shown in block schematic in Fig. 1.2.

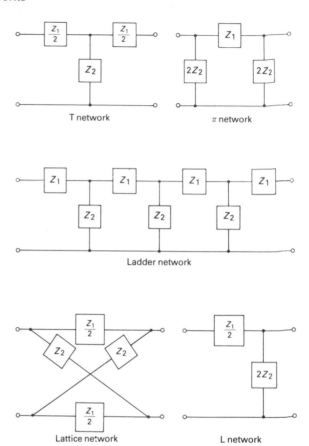

Fig. 1.2

Networks are generally classified as *symmetrical* or *asymmetrical* and are either of the *balanced* or *unbalanced* forms. Symmetrical networks are unchanged when input and output ports are interchanged whereas asymmetrical networks are changed. Networks are 'balanced' when their components are correctly placed with respect to an 'earth plane' so that stray capacitances balance out and produce less interference or 'cross-talk' between circuits.

1.3 Properties of networks

The transmission properties of networks are best described in terms of the attenuation and phase-change coefficients of a network, both of which are functions of frequency.

In addition, it is also necessary to make a more detailed study of the impedances of a network, which have a profound effect on its transmission properties, since generally the telecommunication network consists of inductors and capacitors whose impedances vary with frequency.

A network is therefore characterised by its *iterative* and *image* impedances, which are generally different. The former are important for 'matching' one network to another, while the latter determine the maximum transfer of power through the network.

1.4 Analysis of networks

Assuming that the network contains only linear passive components, the analysis can be done by considering the voltages and currents of the network or its impedances. A set of equations can be established between these quantities and it leads to the basic $A B C D$ parameters* which are well known in power and transistor circuits.

In telecommunication circuits, however, one is more concerned with the transmission properties of the network as a function of frequency. It is usual, therefore, to treat the network in such a way as to bring out these properties in the analysis.

In the case of lossless one-port networks, this will be done by considering the *poles* and *zeros* of the network in the light of Foster's reactance theorem. For two-port networks, usual algebraic methods will be employed, though advanced techniques also employ the concept of poles and zeros, which leads to *modern network theory*; this will be applied to filters in Chapter 4.

1.5 Filter networks

A filter is a special network whose function is to allow signals in certain bands of frequencies to pass easily, while highly attenuating or suppressing adjacent unwanted bands. The band of frequencies passed is called the *pass band* and the band of frequencies attenuated is called the *stop band*.

There are essentially two broad classes of filters known as *analogue* filters and *digital* filters. Analogue filters are used for filtering analogue signals and have been used extensively in the past. These are passive networks which employ R, L and C components to achieve a given design using either image parameter theory or the more modern synthesis approach.

An alternative form of analogue filter which uses *active* networks is known as an *active filter*. These are popular in certain applications, especially at the lower frequencies. One advantage is that heavy and costly inductors can be eliminated and replaced by RC networks, through the use of operational amplifiers, gyrators or negative impedance converters. Moreover, by using active devices such as op amps, insertion loss through

* See Section 3.4.

the network may be compensated for, in addition to obtaining the desired response characteristic.

In recent years, there has been a growing interest in transmitting information in digital form, and the need to process digital signals has led to the development of *digital filters*. The digital signal consisting of time samples of the input signal has a periodic frequency response and so the digital filter must have a similar periodic frequency response in order to preserve the signal samples through the filter. It is achieved by the use of delay elements in the filter. Typical examples of analogue, active and digital filters are shown in Fig. 1.3.

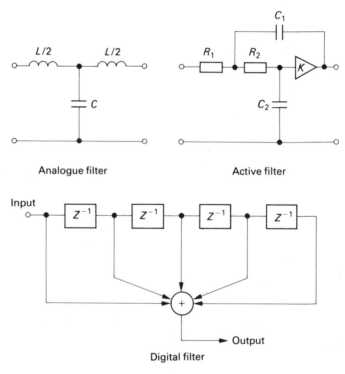

Analogue filter   Active filter

Digital filter

Fig. 1.3

1.6 CCD and SAW filters[1-4]

Two recent developments in the signal processing field are charge-coupled device filters (CCD filters) and surface acoustic wave filters (SAW filters).

The basic charge-coupled device consists of a linear array of closely spaced control electrodes on a continuous silicon-dioxide dielectric layer, which covers the single-crystal silicon substrate material. Information is stored by minority carriers as a charge packet in a potential well under a gate electrode. The charge can be moved to another gate by means of clocked pulses and so the device can operate as a shift register. The charge-coupled device can also be used for transversal filtering and the split-gate electrode transversal filter shown in Fig. 1.4 forms the basis of most signal processing CCD circuits.

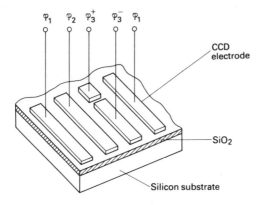

Fig. 1.4

SAW filters also, can offer a transversal signal processing capability because the signal is launched as a slow wave across the surface of a crystal and it can be tapped at any point as it passes down the length of the crystal. The SAW delay line filter shown in Fig. 1.5 consists of a piezoelectric substrate such as a thin slice of quartz or lithium niobate with input and output interdigital transducers. SAW delay line structures can be designed as *matched filters* using the transversal filter approach. The matched filter is used to maximise the output (S/N) ratio at the receiver. Further details of CCD filters and SAW filters are given in Appendix A.

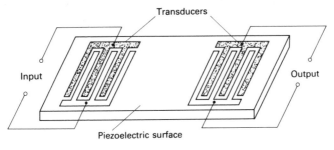

Fig. 1.5

1.7   Miscellaneous filters

In many engineering applications, filters are designed to achieve a specified amplitude response over a given band of frequencies because this is of primary concern. However, in some special cases, filters are designed for certain other characteristics. Typical examples of this are the Bessel filter[5,6] and the Kalman filter[7-10].

In the Bessel filter design which is based on the use of Bessel polynomials, a linear phase characteristic or maximally flat time-delay is realisable at the expense of a poorer amplitude response near cut-off. Such filters are used for the processing of pulse signals in television.

In navigation systems, on the other hand, the Kalman filter which operates in the time-domain may be employed. The filter design is based on a recursive algorithm which minimises the mean-square error estimate of the signal and it is usually evaluated by digital computation.

2
One-port networks

The two most important examples of one-port networks are the series-tuned circuit and the parallel-tuned circuit.

2.1 Series-tuned circuit

Let Z be the input impedance of a series circuit consisting of R, L and C, connected to a generator of variable frequency, as shown in Fig. 2.1. If ω is the angular frequency we have

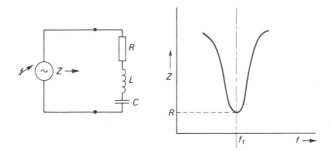

Fig. 2.1

$$Z = R + j\left(\omega L - \frac{1}{\omega C}\right) = \frac{\omega CR + j(\omega^2 LC - 1)}{\omega C} \tag{1}$$

At resonance, $\omega = \omega_r$ and so

$$\omega_r L = \frac{1}{\omega_r C}$$

or

$$\omega_r = \frac{1}{\sqrt{LC}} \tag{2}$$

and

$$f_r = \frac{1}{2\pi\sqrt{LC}}$$

From equations (1) and (2) we obtain when $\omega = \omega_r$

$Z = R$, which is a pure resistance at resonance.

In general, equation (1) can be written as

$$Z = \frac{\omega CR + jLC[\omega^2 - (1/LC)]}{\omega C} = R + j\frac{L}{\omega}(\omega^2 - \omega_r^2) \text{ since } \omega_r^2 = \frac{1}{LC}$$

For a lossless network, $R = 0$, giving

$$Z = j\frac{L}{\omega}(\omega^2 - \omega_r^2) \tag{3}$$

2.2   Parallel-tuned circuit

Let Z be the input impedance of a parallel circuit consisting of L, R and C, where R is in series with the coil and is shown in Fig. 2.2.

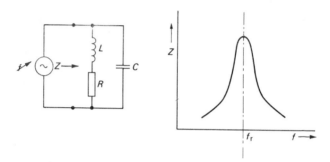

Fig. 2.2

We have

$$Z = \frac{(R + j\omega L)[-j(1/\omega C)]}{R + j[\omega L - (1/\omega C)]} = \frac{R + j\omega L}{j\omega CR + (1 - \omega^2 LC)}$$

Usually $\omega L \gg R$ if the Q of the coil circuit is large where

$$Q = \frac{\omega L}{R}$$

Hence

$$Z = \frac{j\omega L}{j\omega CR + (1 - \omega^2 LC)} \tag{4}$$

At resonance, $\omega = \omega_r$ and

$$\omega_r L = \frac{1}{\omega_r C}$$

or

$$\omega_r = \frac{1}{\sqrt{LC}}$$

and
$$f_r = \frac{1}{2\pi\sqrt{LC}}$$

Hence
$$Z = \frac{j\omega_r L}{j\omega_r CR} = \frac{L}{CR} = Z_d \tag{5}$$

which is called the *dynamic impedance* of the circuit and is a pure resistance.

In general, equation (4) can be written as

$$Z = \frac{j\omega L}{j\omega CR + LC\left(\dfrac{1}{LC} - \omega^2\right)} = \frac{j\omega L}{j\omega CR + LC(\omega_r^2 - \omega^2)}$$

For a lossless network, $R = 0$ giving

$$Z = \frac{j\omega L}{LC(\omega_r^2 - \omega^2)} = \frac{j\omega}{C}\left[\frac{1}{\omega_r^2 - \omega^2}\right]$$

or
$$Z = \frac{\omega}{jC}\left[\frac{1}{\omega^2 - \omega_r^2}\right] \tag{6}$$

Again, from equation (4) we have

$$Z = \frac{j\omega L}{j\omega CR + (1 - \omega^2 LC)}$$

$$= \frac{j\omega L}{j\omega CR\left[1 + \dfrac{LC}{j\omega CR}\left(\dfrac{1}{LC} - \omega^2\right)\right]} = \frac{\dfrac{L}{CR}}{\left[1 + \dfrac{LC}{j\omega CR}\left(\dfrac{1}{LC} - \omega^2\right)\right]}$$

Since
$$Q \simeq \frac{\omega L}{R} \simeq \frac{1}{\omega CR}$$

when ω is *close* to ω_r and we also have

$$LC \simeq \frac{1}{\omega_r^2}$$

Then
$$Z = \frac{L/CR}{1 + (Q/j\omega_r^2)(\omega_r^2 - \omega^2)} = \frac{Z_d}{1 + j(Q/\omega_r^2)(\omega^2 - \omega_r^2)}$$

Now $\omega^2 = (\omega_r \pm \delta\omega)^2 \simeq \omega_r^2 \pm 2\omega_r\,\delta\omega$ since $(\delta\omega)^2$ is very small for values of ω *close* to resonance.

Hence $(\omega^2 - \omega_r^2) = 2\omega_r\,\delta\omega$ (choosing the positive value)

and
$$Z = \frac{Z_d}{1 + 2j\dfrac{Q\,\delta\omega}{\omega_r}} = \frac{Z_d}{1 + 2jQ\alpha}$$

where
$$\alpha = \frac{\delta\omega}{\omega_r} = \frac{\delta f}{f_r}$$

or
$$|Z| = \frac{Z_d}{\sqrt{1 + 4Q^2\alpha^2}} = \frac{L/CR}{\sqrt{1 + 4Q^2\alpha^2}}$$

which gives the general impedance Z *close* to resonance, in terms of Z_d, Q and α. The 3 dB bandwidth of the tuned circuit is defined between the two frequencies for which we have

$$|Z|/Z_d = \frac{1}{\sqrt{2}} = \frac{1}{\sqrt{1 + 4Q^2\alpha^2}}$$

with
$$1 + 4Q^2\alpha^2 = 2$$

or
$$\alpha = \frac{1}{2Q} \text{ (positive value only)}$$

Thus
$$\text{bandwidth} = 2\delta f = 2\alpha f_r$$

or
$$\text{bandwidth} = \frac{f_r}{Q}$$

Example 2.1

A constant-voltage generator is connected to a parallel-tuned circuit consisting of a coil of inductance 250 μH and resistance 12.5 Ω in parallel with a variable capacitor. For the circuit whose resonant frequency is 1 MHz, calculate its impedance at 4 kHz off resonance.

Solution
We have

$$f_r = \frac{1}{2\pi\sqrt{LC}}$$

or
$$C = \frac{1}{4\pi^2 L f_r^2} = \frac{1}{4\pi^2 \times 250 \times 10^{-6} \times 10^{12}} \simeq 100 \text{ pf}$$

Now
$$Q = \omega_r\frac{L}{R} = \frac{2\pi \times 10^6 \times 250 \times 10^{-6}}{12.5} = 40\pi \simeq 125$$

Also
$$Z_d = \frac{L}{CR} = \frac{250 \times 10^{-6}}{100 \times 10^{-12} \times 12\cdot5} = 200 \text{ k}\Omega$$

and
$$Z = \frac{Z_d}{\sqrt{1 + 4Q^2 \delta^2}}$$

where
$$\alpha = \frac{\delta \omega_r}{\omega_r} = \frac{\delta f_r}{f_r} = \frac{4000}{10^6} = \frac{1}{250}$$

Now
$$\sqrt{1 + 4Q^2 \delta^2} = \sqrt{1 + 4(125)^2 \frac{1}{(250)^2}} = \sqrt{2}$$

Hence
$$Z = \frac{200 \text{ k}\Omega}{\sqrt{2}}$$

or
$$Z = 140 \text{ k}\Omega$$

Comment

Since $Z = 140 \text{ k}\Omega$ corresponds to $Z_d / \sqrt{2}$, the 3 dB bandwidth of the tuned circuit is $2 \times 4 \text{ kHz} = 8 \text{ kHz}$.

2.3 Lossless networks

The input impedance Z of a one-port lossless network may assume the forms given by equations (3) and (6). These can be combined to give a single general expression for any combination of such networks and the input impedance is of the form

$$Z = \pm A \left[\frac{(\omega^2 - \omega_1^2)(\omega^2 - \omega_3^2) \cdots}{(\omega^2 - \omega_2^2)(\omega^2 - \omega_4^2) \cdots} \right] \tag{7}$$

where $A = j\omega H$ or $H/j\omega$, H being a scale factor.

An alternative form for Z can be obtained by using the complex variable $s = \sigma + j\omega$, with $\sigma = 0$ for a lossless network. Hence we obtain,

$$Z = \pm A \left[\frac{(s^2 + \omega_1^2)(s^2 + \omega_3^2) \cdots}{(s^2 + \omega_2^2)(s^2 + \omega_4^2) \cdots} \right] \tag{8}$$

where $A = sH$ or H/s, H being a scale factor. In both the expressions above, the $\pm$ signs may be omitted for convenience.

2.4 Poles and zeros

The values of ω which make $Z = 0$ in (7) such as ω_1, ω_3 etc. are called the *zeros* of Z and are denoted by a small circle 'o'. Similarly, the values of ω which make $Z = \infty$ such as ω_2, ω_4 etc. are called the *poles* of Z and are denoted by a cross '×'.

Poles and zeros can be plotted along the X-axis, with reactance $\pm jX$, along the Y-axis in the ω-plane or alternatively, in the complex s-plane, as shown in Fig. 2.3. The concept of poles and zeros is of great importance in modern network theory and in the field of control engineering.

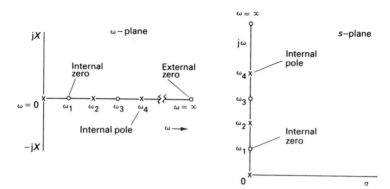

Fig. 2.3

2.5 Foster's reactance theorem[11,12]

Much information about the behaviour of a lossless network may be obtained from a study of its poles and zeros and this is concisely expressed by Foster's reactance theorem as follows.

The input impedance of any one-port lossless network is completely specified by its internal poles and zeros which occur at real frequencies and by a scale factor H, which is a real constant.

As a result of this theorem, two useful rules may be stated.

Rule 1 The poles and zeros of a one-port lossless network must alternate along the frequency axis. This is called the separation property.

Rule 2 Four types of reactance curves may be obtained with a lossless one-port network.

Notes

1. $\omega = 0$ is called an *external* pole and $\omega = \infty$ is called an *external* zero in Fig. 2.3.
2. $\omega_1, \omega_2, \omega_3 \ldots$ etc. are the *internal* poles and zeros and by Rule 1 above, the separation property implies that $\omega_1 < \omega_2 < \omega_3$ etc.
3. Foster's reactance theorem does not apply to the *external* poles and zeros, but it is useful to consider them first when drawing reactance curves.
4. The input impedance of a network is also called the driving-point impedance.

(a) Foster networks

The four possible forms depend upon the position of the poles and zeros along the frequency axis (see Figs. 2.4 and 2.5).

Form A

$$Z = j\omega H \left[\frac{(\omega^2 - \omega_2^2)(\omega^2 - \omega_4^2) \cdots (\omega^2 - \omega_{2z}^2)}{(\omega^2 - \omega_1^2)(\omega^2 - \omega_3^2) \cdots (\omega^2 - \omega_{2z+1}^2)} \right]$$

where z is a real number.

Form B

$$Z = j\omega H \left[\frac{(\omega^2 - \omega_2^2)(\omega^2 - \omega_4^2) \cdots (\omega^2 - \omega_{2z}^2)}{(\omega^2 - \omega_1^2)(\omega^2 - \omega_3^2) \cdots (\omega^2 - \omega_{2z-1}^2)} \right]$$

Form C

$$Z = \frac{H}{j\omega} \left[\frac{(\omega^2 - \omega_1^2)(\omega^2 - \omega_3^2) \cdots (\omega^2 - \omega_{2p+1}^2)}{(\omega^2 - \omega_2^2)(\omega^2 - \omega_4^2) \cdots (\omega^2 - \omega_{2p}^2)} \right]$$

where p is a real number.

Form D

$$Z = \frac{H}{j\omega} \left[\frac{(\omega^2 - \omega_1^2)(\omega^2 - \omega_3^2) \cdots (\omega^2 - \omega_{2p-1}^2)}{(\omega^2 - \omega_2^2)(\omega^2 - \omega_4^2) \cdots (\omega^2 - \omega_{2p}^2)} \right]$$

For these expressions, four different series-type networks can be constructed and are called the *canonic** forms or *first* Foster forms. By the use of admittance methods or by the principle of duality, four parallel-type or dual networks can be constructed and are called the *second* Foster forms. The various networks and their associated reactance curves are shown in Figs. 2.4 and 2.5. For convenience, assume $z = p = 2$, as this would restrict the number of terms in Z to about two or three.

First Foster networks

Type 1

$$Z = j\omega H \left[\frac{(\omega^2 - \omega_2^2)}{(\omega^2 - \omega_1^2)(\omega^2 - \omega_3^2)} \right]$$

Type 2

$$Z = j\omega H \left[\frac{(\omega^2 - \omega_2^2)}{(\omega^2 - \omega_1^2)} \right]$$

Type 3

$$Z = \frac{H}{j\omega} \left[\frac{(\omega^2 - \omega_1^2)(\omega^2 - \omega_3^2)}{(\omega^2 - \omega_2^2)} \right]$$

---

* Networks with a minimum number of elements are called canonic.

Type 4

$$Z = \frac{H}{j\omega}\left[\frac{(\omega^2 - \omega_1^2)}{(\omega^2 - \omega_2^2)}\right]$$

Second Foster networks
It is more useful to draw reactance curves, though by using admittance methods we could also draw susceptance curves if required.

Type 5

$$Z = \frac{H}{j\omega}\left[\frac{(\omega^2 - \omega_1^2)(\omega^2 - \omega_3^2)}{(\omega^2 - \omega_2^2)}\right]$$

Type 6

$$Z = \frac{H}{j\omega}\left[\frac{(\omega^2 - \omega_1^2)}{(\omega^2 - \omega_2^2)}\right]$$

Type 7

$$Z = j\omega H\left[\frac{(\omega^2 - \omega_2^2)}{(\omega^2 - \omega_1^2)(\omega^2 - \omega_3^2)}\right]$$

Type 8

$$Z = j\omega H\left[\frac{(\omega^2 - \omega_2^2)}{(\omega^2 - \omega_1^2)}\right]$$

(b) Synthesis of Foster networks
The synthesis of a network to give a certain reactance curve, can be determined by expanding the equation for Z as partial fractions and identifying each fraction as a physical component. This is illustrated by the following example.

Example 2.2
Synthesize a series Foster network with two internal poles at ω_1 and ω_3 and one internal zero at ω_2 to give the reactance curves of Type 1 in Section 2.5(a).

Solution

Here
$$Z = j\omega H\left[\frac{(\omega^2 - \omega_2^2)}{(\omega^2 - \omega_1^2)(\omega^2 - \omega_3^2)}\right]$$

Let
$$\frac{(\omega^2 - \omega_2^2)}{(\omega^2 - \omega_1^2)(\omega^2 - \omega_3^2)} = \frac{A}{(\omega^2 - \omega_1^2)} + \frac{B}{(\omega^2 - \omega_2^2)}$$

Hence
$$(\omega^2 - \omega_2^2) \equiv A(\omega^2 - \omega_3^2) + B(\omega^2 - \omega_1^2)$$

Putting
$\omega = \omega_1$ gives $\omega_1^2 - \omega_2^2 \equiv A(\omega_1^2 - \omega_3^2)$

or
$$A = (\omega_1^2 - \omega_2^2)/(\omega_1^2 - \omega_3^2)$$

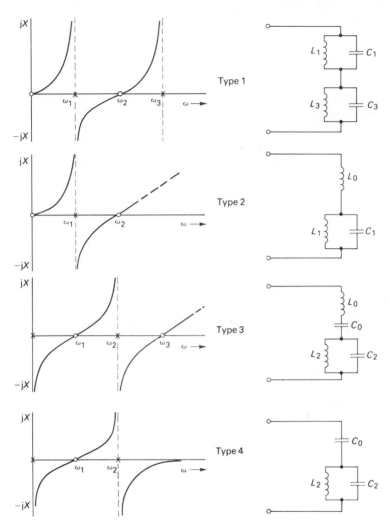

Fig. 2.4

Similarly, if $\omega = \omega_3$ gives

$$\omega_3^2 - \omega_2^2 \equiv B(\omega_3^2 - \omega_1^2)$$

or

$$B = \frac{(\omega_3^2 - \omega_2^2)}{(\omega_3^2 - \omega_1^2)}$$

and

$$Z = \frac{j\omega HA}{(\omega^2 - \omega_1^2)} + \frac{j\omega HB}{(\omega^2 - \omega_3^2)}$$

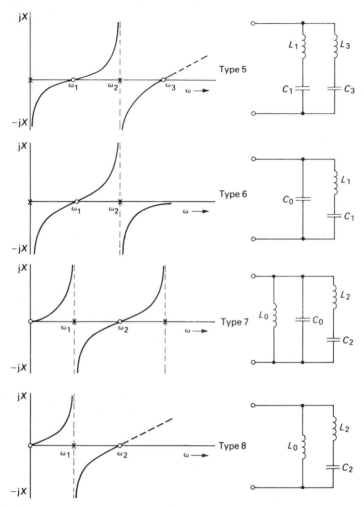

Fig. 2.5

Substituting the values for A and B leads to

$$Z = \frac{j\omega H(\omega_1^2 - \omega_2^2)}{(\omega_1^2 - \omega_3^2)(\omega^2 - \omega_1^2)} + \frac{j\omega H(\omega_3^2 - \omega_2^2)}{(\omega_3^2 - \omega_1^2)(\omega^2 - \omega_3^2)}$$

Comments
1. In typical problems A and B usually have numerical values.
2. The right-hand side of the equation for Z corresponds to two *series* impedances, each of which can be identified as a *parallel* combination of L and C from Table 2.1.

In a typical case the numerical values of ω_1, ω_2 and ω_3 would be given and the scale factor H is evaluated from data specifying the value of Z at some particular ω. The component values are then obtained with the help of the equations

$$\omega_1^2 = \frac{1}{L_1 C_1} \quad \text{and} \quad \omega_3^2 = \frac{1}{L_3 C_3}$$

The network is shown in Fig. 2.6.

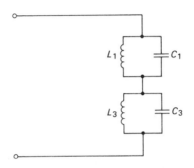

Fig. 2.6

Comment
To synthesize the second Foster form, express the result as the sum of two admittances Y_1 and Y_2 and identify the components from the admittance column in Table 2.1.

Example 2.3
Design a series-type Foster network to have an impedance j500 at $\omega = 0.5 \times 10^6$ rad/s. There is to be a pole at $\omega = 1.0 \times 10^6$ rad/s and a zero at $\omega = 2.0 \times 10^6$ rad/s.

Solution
Let
$$\omega_1 = 1.0 \times 10^6 \text{ rad/s}$$
$$\omega_2 = 2.0 \times 10^6 \text{ rad/s}$$

Since the impedance has a positive value at $\omega = 0.5 \times 10^6$ rad/s, it must decrease to zero at $\omega = 0$. Hence, there is an *external* zero at $\omega = 0$ and the type can be identified as Type 2 of Section 2.5(a).

Hence
$$Z = j\omega H \left[\frac{(\omega^2 - \omega_2^2)}{(\omega^2 - \omega_1^2)} \right]$$

or
$$j500 = j0.5 \times 10^6 \times H \left[\frac{(0.5 \times 10^6)^2 - (2 \times 10^6)^2}{(0.5 \times 10^6)^2 - (1 \times 10^6)^2} \right]$$

$$= j0.5 \times 10^6 \times H \left[\frac{(0.25) - 4}{(0.25) - 1} \right]$$

$$= j0.5 \times 10^6 H \times \tfrac{15}{3}$$

or $$H = 2 \times 10^{-4}$$

Now let $$\frac{\omega^2 - \omega_2^2}{\omega^2 - \omega_1^2} = 1 + \frac{A}{\omega^2 - \omega_1^2}$$

or $$\omega^2 - \omega_2^2 = \omega^2 - \omega_1^2 + A$$

If $\omega = \omega_1$ then

$$A = \omega_1^2 - \omega_2^2 = (1.0 \times 10^6)^2 - (2 \times 10^6)^2 = -3 \times 10^{12}$$

Hence $$Z = j\omega H \left[1 + \frac{A}{\omega^2 - \omega_1^2} \right]$$

$$= j\omega \times 2 \times 10^{-4} - \frac{j\omega \times 6 \times 10^8}{(\omega^2 - \omega_1^2)}$$

or $$Z = j\omega \times 2 \times 10^{-4} + \frac{\omega \times 6 \times 10^8}{j(\omega^2 - \omega_1^2)}$$

Table 2.1

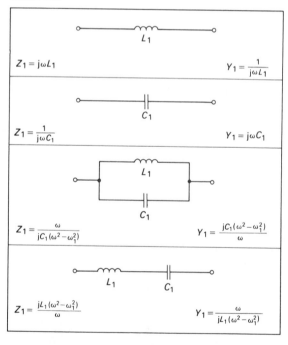

$Z_1 = j\omega L_1$		$Y_1 = \dfrac{1}{j\omega L_1}$
$Z_1 = \dfrac{1}{j\omega C_1}$		$Y_1 = j\omega C_1$
$Z_1 = \dfrac{\omega}{jC_1(\omega^2 - \omega_1^2)}$		$Y_1 = \dfrac{jC_1(\omega^2 - \omega_1^2)}{\omega}$
$Z_1 = \dfrac{jL_1(\omega^2 - \omega_1^2)}{\omega}$		$Y_1 = \dfrac{\omega}{jL_1(\omega^2 - \omega_1^2)}$

From Table 2.1 this corresponds to an inductance L in series with a parallel L_1 and C_1.

Hence $$L = 2 \times 10^{-4} \text{ H}$$

and $$C_1 = \frac{1}{6 \times 10^8} = 1700\,\text{pf}$$

Now $$\omega_1^2 = \frac{1}{L_1 C_1}$$

or $$L_1 = \frac{1}{(1 \times 10^6)^2 \times 1700 \times 10^{-12}} = 0.6\,\text{mH}$$

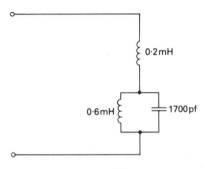

Fig. 2.7

Example 2.4

State and explain Foster's reactance theorem. Sketch the variation of reactance with frequency for the loss-free one-port network in Fig. 2.8. Express the reactance X in the form

$$X = \frac{k}{\omega} \frac{(\omega^2 - \omega_1^2)(\omega^2 - \omega_3^2)}{(\omega^2 - \omega_2^2)}$$

and derive expressions for k, ω_1, ω_2 and ω_3 in terms of L_1, C_1, L_3 and C_3.

(U.L.)

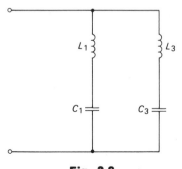

Fig. 2.8

Solution
The answer to the first part of the question will be found in Section 2.5.

The expression for X shows that the network has zeros at ω_1 and ω_3 and a pole at ω_2. Also, the input impedance (or reactance) tends to a large value at $\omega = 0$ and $\omega = \infty$ and so these are the external poles. Hence, the reactance diagram can be drawn as in Fig. 2.9.

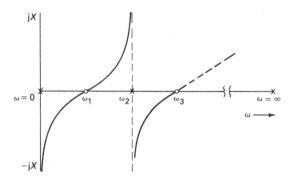

Fig. 2.9

The input impedance of the network is by inspection

$$Z = \frac{Z_1 Z_2}{Z_1 + Z_2}$$

with

$$Z_1 = j[\omega L_1 - (1/\omega)C_1]$$
$$Z_2 = j[\omega L_3 - (1/\omega)C_3]$$

Hence

$$jX = \frac{j[\omega L_1 - (1/\omega)C_1] \cdot j[\omega L_3 - (1/\omega)C_3]}{j[\omega(L_1 + L_3) - 1/\omega(1/C_1 + 1/C_3)]}$$

or

$$X = \frac{1}{\omega} \cdot \frac{[(\omega^2 L_1 C_1 - 1)(\omega^2 L_3 C_3 - 1)]}{[\omega^2(L_1 + L_3)C_1 C_3 - (C_1 + C_3)]}$$

$$= \frac{1}{\omega} \cdot \frac{L_1 C_1 \cdot L_3 C_3[(\omega^2 - 1/L_1 C_1)(\omega^2 - 1/L_3 C_3)]}{(L_1 + L_3)[\omega^2 - (C_1 + C_3)/C_1 C_3(L_1 + L_3)]}$$

$$= \frac{L_1 L_3}{\omega(L_1 + L_3)}\left[\frac{[\omega^2 - (1/L_1 C_1)][\omega^2 - (1/L_3 C_3)]}{\omega^2 - (C_1 + C_3)/C_1 C_3(L_1 + L_3)}\right]$$

Equating this to the expression given we have

$$\frac{k}{\omega}\frac{(\omega^2 - \omega_1^2)(\omega^2 - \omega_3^2)}{(\omega^2 - \omega_2^2)} \equiv \frac{L_1 L_3}{\omega(L_1 + L_3)}\left[\frac{[\omega^2 - (1/L_1 C_1)][\omega^2 - (1/L_3 C_3)]}{\omega^2 - (C_1 + C_3)/C_1 C_3(L_1 + L_3)}\right]$$

Hence

$$k = L_1 L_3/(L_1 + L_3)$$

$$\omega_1 = \frac{1}{\sqrt{L_1 C_1}}$$

$$\omega_2 = \sqrt{(C_1 + C_3)/C_1 C_3 (L_1 + L_3)} = \sqrt{\frac{1}{(L_1 + L_3)C_1 C_3/(C_1 + C_3)}}$$

$$\omega_3 = \frac{1}{\sqrt{L_3 C_3}}$$

(c) Synthesis of Cauer networks*

This method uses the ladder-type network and the continued fraction expansion, which yields two canonic forms[13, 14]. As an example, consider the general ladder network shown in Fig. 2.10 with series arms expressed as impedances and shunt arms as admittances.

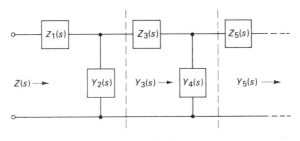

Fig. 2.10

Here
$$Z(s) = Z_1(s) + \frac{1}{Y_2(s) + Y_3(s)}$$

$$= Z_1(s) + \cfrac{1}{Y_2(s) + \cfrac{1}{Z_3(s) + \cfrac{1}{Y_4(s) + Y_5(s)}}}$$

The expression on the right-hand side is called a continued fraction expansion in which every other term is either an impedance or an admittance of the given ladder network to be synthesized.

Hence, by writing the given expression for Z in terms of an expansion like this, we can identify each of the components of the network.

---

* These networks are due to the pioneering work of W. Cauer.

Since $Z_1(s)$ is an inductance, it contains a term in s only and has a pole at $s = \infty$. By writing $Z_1(s)$ separately, it amounts to 'removing a pole' from Z and obtaining the remainder $Z - Z_1(s) = 1/[Y_2(s) + Y_3(s)]$.

$Y_3(s)$ is then inverted and another pole $Z_3(s)$ is removed to leave the remainder $1/[Y_4(s) + Y_5(s)]$ and so on.

This technique yields one of the canonic forms and by removing 'zeros' rather than 'poles', an alternative canonic form can be obtained. It is best illustrated in the following example.

Example 2.5

Synthesize the two types of Cauer networks shown in Fig. 2.11 which have the input impedance $Z(s)$ given by

$$Z(s) = \frac{3s^4 + 45s^2 + 50}{s^3 + 10s}$$

where $s = j\omega$.

First form

Carrying out the division starting with the *highest* power in s first, we obtain

$$s^3 + 10s)3s^4 + 45s^2 + 50(3s \to Z_1(s)$$
$$\underline{3s^4 + 30s^2}$$
$$15s^2 + 50)s^3 + 10s(s/15 \to Y_2(s)$$
$$\underline{s^3 + \tfrac{10}{3}s}$$
$$\tfrac{20}{3}s)15s^2 + 50(9s/4 \to Z_3(s)$$
$$\underline{15s^2}$$
$$50)\tfrac{20}{3}s(\tfrac{2}{15}s \to Y_4(s)$$
$$\underline{\tfrac{20}{3}s}$$

Second form

Carrying out the division starting with the *lowest* power in s first, we obtain

$$10s + s^3)50 + 45s^2 + 3s^4(5/s \to Z_1(s)$$
$$\underline{50 + 5s^2}$$
$$40s^2 + 3s^4)10s + s^3(\tfrac{1}{4}s \to Y_2(s)$$
$$\underline{10s + \tfrac{3}{4}s^3}$$
$$s^3/4)40s^2 + 3s^4(160/s \to Z_3(s)$$
$$\underline{40s^2}$$
$$3s^4)s^3/4(\tfrac{1}{12}s \to Y_4(s)$$
$$\underline{s^3/4}$$

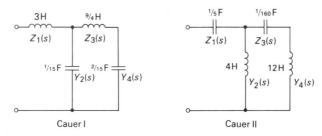

Fig. 2.11

Comments
1. Arranging $Z(s)$ in *descending* powers of s (first form) ensures that the first term of the quotient will be a term in s to give a pole at $s = \infty$, i.e. *poles* at infinity are being removed by the division.
2. Arranging $Z(s)$ in *ascending* powers of s (second form) ensures that the first term of the quotient will be a term in $1/s$ to give a zero at $s = \infty$, i.e. *zeros* at infinity are being removed by the division.

Example 2.6
(a)   State the conditions that must be satisfied for a driving-point impedance function to be physically realisable using passive linear components.
(b)   Synthesize *two* one-port networks to have the impedance function

$$Z(s) = \frac{2s(s^2+4)}{(s^2+2)(s^2+6)} \qquad \text{(C.E.I.)}$$

Solution
(a)   For a driving-point impedance function $Z(s)$ to be physically realisable, with passive linear components, it must be a *positive real* function which satisfies the following conditions.

(1) $Z(s)$ is real for real values of s.
(2)   Re $Z(s) \geqslant 0$ for Re $s \geqslant 0$ where Re signifies 'the real part of'.

These conditions are satisfied if the following criteria are present.

(1) $Z(s)$ has no poles in the right-half s-plane.
(2)   All the poles of $Z(s)$ on the $j\omega$-axis are simple and have real residues.
(3)   The real part of $Z(j\omega)$ is $\geqslant 0$ for all values of ω.
(b)   We have

$$Z(s) = \frac{2s(s^2+4)}{(s^2+2)(s^2+6)}$$

or

$$\frac{Z(s)}{2s} = \frac{(s^2+4)}{(s^2+2)(s^2+6)} = \frac{A}{(s^2+2)} + \frac{B}{(s^2+6)}$$

Thus

$$(s^2+4) \equiv A(s^2+6) + B(s^2+2)$$

with
$$1 = A + B \tag{1}$$
$$4 = 6A + 2B \tag{2}$$

From equations (1) and (2) we obtain
$$A = 1/2$$
$$B = 1/2$$

with
$$Z(s) = \frac{s}{(s^2 + 2)} + \frac{s}{(s^2 + 6)}$$

From Table 2.1, each term represents a parallel combination of L and C. Hence
$$\omega_1^2 = \frac{1}{L_1 C_1} = 2$$

with $C_1 = 1\,\text{F}$ and so $L_1 = (1/2)\,\text{H}$. Also,
$$\omega_3^2 = \frac{1}{L_3 C_3} = 6$$

with $C_3 = 1\,\text{F}$ and so $L_3 = (1/6)\,\text{H}$. The first network is shown in Fig. 2.12 (a).

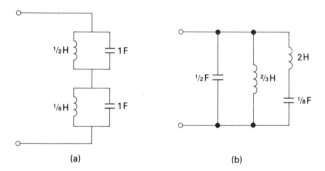

(a)　　　　(b)

Fig. 2.12

Also, we have
$$Y(s) = \frac{1}{Z(s)} = \frac{(s^2 + 2)(s^2 + 6)}{2s(s^2 + 4)}$$

with
$$\frac{2Y(s)}{s} = \frac{(s^2 + 2)(s^2 + 6)}{s^2(s^2 + 4)} = \frac{s^4 + 8s^2 + 12}{s^4 + 4s^2}$$

or
$$\frac{2Y(s)}{s} = 1 + \frac{(4s^2 + 12)}{s^2(s^2 + 4)} = 1 + \frac{A}{s^2} + \frac{B}{(s^2 + 4)}$$

Thus
$$s^4 + 8s^2 + 12 \equiv s^4 + 4s^2 + A(s^2 + 4) + Bs^2$$

with
$$8 = 4 + A + B \tag{3}$$
$$12 = 4A \tag{4}$$

From equations (3) and (4) we obtain
$$A = 3$$
$$B = 1$$

with
$$\frac{2Y(s)}{s} = 1 + \frac{3}{s^2} + \frac{1}{(s^2 + 4)}$$

or
$$Y(s) = \frac{s}{2} + \frac{3}{2s} + \frac{s}{2(s^2 + 4)}$$

From Table 2.1, the first term represents a capacitance of $(1/2)$ F, the second term represents an inductance of $(2/3)$ H and the third term represents a series L, C circuit with $L = 2\,\mathrm{H}$, $\omega^2 = 1/LC = 4$ and so $C = (1/8)\,\mathrm{F}$. The network is shown in Fig. 2.12(b).

2.6 *RC* and *RL* networks[15, 16]

As in the case of *LC* networks, *RC* and *RL* networks can also be synthesized using the Foster and Cauer canonic forms.

(a) *RC* networks

The two Foster forms involve partial fraction expansions, the first form yielding the driving-point impedance function $Z_{RC}(s)$ and the second form yielding the driving-point admittance function $Y_{RC}(s)$. Thus, we obtain

$$Z_{RC}(s) = \frac{k_0}{s} + \sum_{i=1}^{n} \frac{k_i}{(s + \sigma_i)} + k_\infty \qquad \text{(Foster I)}$$

and

$$Y_{RC}(s) = k_0 + \sum_{i=1}^{n} \frac{k_i s}{(s + \sigma_i)} + s k_\infty \qquad \text{(Foster II)}$$

The various immittance terms are identified from the two Foster networks shown in Fig. 2.13.

The two Cauer forms involve both impedance and admittance functions, and are given by continued fraction expansions. Thus, we obtain

$$Z_{RC}(s) = Z_1 + \cfrac{1}{\cfrac{1}{Z_2} + \cfrac{1}{Z_3 + \ldots}} \qquad \text{(Cauer I)}$$

and

$$Y_{RC}(s) = Y_1 + \cfrac{1}{\cfrac{1}{Y_2} + \cfrac{1}{Y_3 + \ldots}} \qquad \text{(Cauer II)}$$

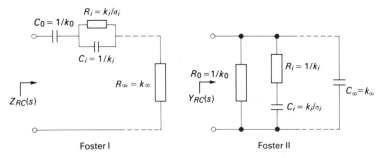

Fig. 2.13

The various immittance terms are identified from the two Cauer ladder networks shown in Fig. 2.14.

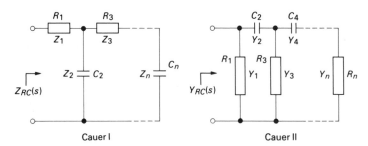

Fig. 2.14

(b)   RL networks

Since the admittance of an inductor is similar to the impedance of a capacitor, it follows that the properties of an RL admittance function are identical to those of an RC impedance function and vice versa. Thus we obtain

$$Y_{RL}(s) = Z_{RC}(s)$$

and

$$Z_{RL}(s) = Y_{RC}(s)$$

with

$$Y_{RL}(s) = \frac{k_0}{s} + \sum_{i=1}^{n} \frac{k_i}{(s+\sigma_i)} + k_\infty \qquad \text{(Foster I)}$$

and

$$Z_{RL}(s) = k_0 + \sum_{i=1}^{n} \frac{k_i s}{(s+\sigma_i)} + s k_\infty \qquad \text{(Foster II)}$$

The two Foster configurations are shown in Fig. 2.15 and the two Cauer configurations are shown in Fig. 2.16.

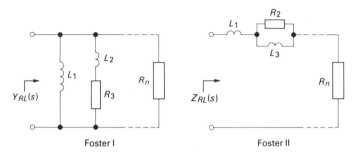

Fig. **2.15**

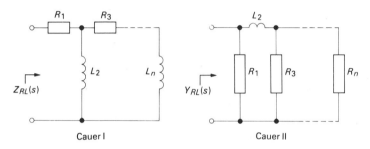

Fig. **2.16**

Comments
1. The poles and zeros of $Z_{RC}(s)$ and $Y_{RC}(s)$ are simple, and alternate on the negative real axis.
2. The factors k_0, k_1, k_2 etc. are known as the residues at the respective poles σ_0, σ_1, σ_2 etc.
3. Typical graphs of $Z_{RC}(\sigma)$ and $Y_{RC}(\sigma)$ are shown in Fig. 2.17.

Example 2.7
(a) Synthesize the first Foster network for the *RC* driving-point impedance function given by

$$Z(s) = \frac{(s+3)(s+5)}{(s+2)(s+4)}$$

(b) Synthesize the first Cauer network for the *RL* driving-point admittance function given by

$$Y(s) = \frac{(2s+1)(2s+3)}{4s(s+1)(s+2)}$$

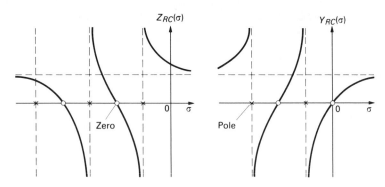

Fig. 2.17

Solution

(a) We have

$$Z(s) = \frac{(s+3)(s+5)}{(s+2)(s+4)} = \frac{s^2 + 8s + 15}{s^2 + 6s + 8}$$

or

$$Z(s) = 1 + \frac{A}{(s+2)} + \frac{B}{(s+4)}$$

Hence

$$s^2 + 8s + 15 = (s+2)(s+4) + A(s+4) + B(s+2)$$

with

$$8 = 6 + A + B \tag{1}$$

$$2 = A + B \tag{2}$$

$$15 = 8 + 4A + 2B \tag{3}$$

From equations (1), (2) and (3) we obtain

$$A = 3/2$$

$$B = 1/2$$

Thus

$$Z(s) = 1 + \frac{3/2}{(s+2)} + \frac{1/2}{(s+4)}$$

where

$$Z(s) = 1 + \frac{k_1}{(s+\sigma_1)} + \frac{k_2}{(s+\sigma_2)}$$

Hence

$$k_1 = 3/2 \qquad k_2 = 1/2$$

$$\sigma_1 = 2 \qquad \sigma_2 = 4$$

and the network is shown in Fig. 2.18(a).

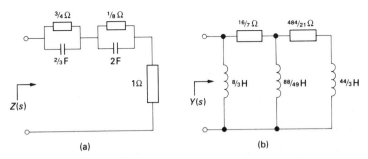

Fig. 2.18

(b)   We have

$$Y(s) = \frac{(2s+1)(2s+3)}{4s(s+1)(s+2)} = \frac{3+8s+4s^2}{8s+12s^2+4s^3}$$

By a continued fraction expansion we obtain

$$8s + 12s^2 + 4s^3)3 + 8s + 4s^2(3/8s \to Y_1(s)$$
$$\underline{3 + \tfrac{9}{2}s + \tfrac{3}{2}s^2}$$
$$\tfrac{7}{2}s + \tfrac{5}{2}s^2)8s + 12s^2 + 4s^3(16/7 \to Z_2(s)$$
$$\underline{8s + \tfrac{40}{7}s^2}$$
$$\tfrac{44}{7}s^2 + 4s^3$$

and continuing with the expansion we obtain

$$44s^2 + 4s^3)\tfrac{7}{2}s + \tfrac{5}{2}s^2(49/88s \to Y_3(s)$$
$$\underline{\tfrac{7}{2}s + \tfrac{49}{22}s^2}$$
$$\tfrac{3}{11}s^2)\tfrac{44}{7}s^2 + 4s^3(484/21 \to Z_4(s)$$
$$\underline{\tfrac{44}{7}s^2}$$
$$4s^3)\tfrac{3}{11}s^2(3/44s \to Y_5(s)$$
$$\tfrac{3}{11}s^2$$

The *RL* network is shown in Fig. 2.18(b).

3
Two-port networks

3.1 Symmetrical networks

A symmetrical two-port network has an input port and an output port. The input and output ports are similar and may be interchanged. Its two most important properties are the characteristic impedance Z_0 and propagation coefficient γ.

(a) Characteristic impedance
This is defined as the input impedance of an infinite number of two-port networks in cascade or of one network terminated in Z_0. It is illustrated in Fig. 3.1.

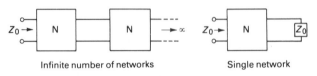

Infinite number of networks   Single network

Fig. 3.1

(b) Propagation coefficient
It is also known as the iterative transfer coefficient and defined as the natural logarithm of the ratio of input and output currents of a network terminated on an iterative basis at both ends, i.e. in Z_0.

Consider the network of Fig. 3.2 with an input current I_S and an output current I_R. In general, I_S will be greater than I_R and will have an angle different from I_S. The ratio I_S/I_R is therefore a complex vector quantity and can be written as e^{γ} where γ is a complex quantity.

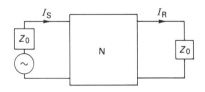

Fig. 3.2

Hence, let $$I_S/I_R = e^\gamma = e^{\alpha+j\beta} = e^\alpha \cdot e^{j\beta} = e^\alpha\underline{/\beta}$$

where $$\gamma = \alpha + j\beta$$

We have $$\left|\frac{I_S}{I_R}\right| = e^\alpha$$

or $$\alpha = \log_e \left|\frac{I_S}{I_R}\right| \text{ nepers}$$

Now 1 neper = 8·686 dB, giving

$$\alpha = 2\text{·}3 \times 8\text{·}686 \log_{10} \left|\frac{I_S}{I_R}\right| \text{ dB}$$

or $$\alpha = 20 \log_{10} \left|\frac{I_S}{I_R}\right| \text{ dB}$$

Since α is responsible for the attenuation of the network it is called the *attenuation coefficient*. The phase shift through the network is due to β which is called the *phase-change coefficient* and it is measured in radians or degrees. For a network like a low-pass filter, the value of β can be negative, due to a phase lag.

Comments
For n similar networks in cascade we have:
 (i)   total attenuation $= \alpha + \alpha + \ldots = n\alpha$ nepers or decibels,
 (ii) total phase shift $= \beta + \beta + \ldots = n\beta$ radians or degrees.

(c) Insertion loss
When the network of Fig. 3.3 is inserted between a generator and load, there is a loss of power in the load due to the mismatch between the generator and network, the network and load and the attenuation through the network. The total loss is called the insertion loss. Hence the insertion loss is the sum of the mismatch losses and attenuation loss.

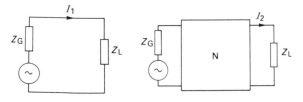

Fig. 3.3

If P_1 is the power in the load without the network inserted and P_2 is the power in the load with the network inserted, the insertion loss is defined as

$$\text{insertion loss} = 10 \log \frac{P_1}{P_2} \text{ dB}$$

Here

$$P_1 = I_1^2 Z_L \qquad \text{(real part)}$$

$$P_2 = I_2^2 Z_L \qquad \text{(real part)}$$

Hence $$\text{insertion loss} = 10 \log \frac{|I_1^2|}{|I_2^2|} = 20 \log_{10} \frac{|I_1|}{|I_2|} \text{ dB}$$

where I_1, I_2 are the load currents *without* the network inserted and *with* the network inserted, respectively.

3.2   Typical networks

(a)   General ladder network
For the configuration shown in Fig. 3.4 we have for the nth mesh

$$(-I_{n-1}) \cdot Z_2 + I_n Z_2 + I_n Z_1 + I_n Z_2 - (I_{n+1}) \cdot Z_2 = 0$$

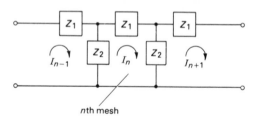

nth mesh

Fig. 3.4

Dividing through by $-2Z_2 I_n$ gives

$$\left\{ \frac{I_{n-1}}{2I_n} \right\} - \frac{(Z_1 + 2Z_2)}{2Z_2} + \frac{I_{n+1}}{2I_n} = 0$$

By definition,

$$\frac{I_{n-1}}{I_n} = e^\gamma \quad \text{and} \quad \frac{I_n}{I_{n+1}} = e^\gamma$$

Hence $$\frac{e^\gamma}{2} + \frac{e^{-\gamma}}{2} = 1 + \frac{Z_1}{2Z_2}$$

or $$\cosh \gamma = 1 + \frac{Z_1}{2Z_2}$$

and
$$\gamma = \cosh^{-1}\left(1 + \frac{Z_1}{2Z_2}\right)$$

from which γ can be evaluated.

Comment
This expression is also valid for a T or π network, since a ladder network can be subdivided into a series of T or π networks.

(b) T network
Let Z_{0T} be the characteristic impedance of the network in Fig. 3.5 which is correctly terminated.

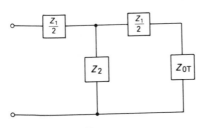

Fig. 3.5

We have
$$Z_i = \frac{Z_1}{2} + \frac{Z_2\left(\dfrac{Z_1}{2} + Z_{0T}\right)}{Z_2 + \dfrac{Z_1}{2} + Z_{0T}}$$

which equals Z_{0T} by definition.
    Hence, expanding the right-hand side and equating to Z_{0T} gives

$$\frac{Z_1 Z_2}{2} + \frac{Z_1^2}{4} + \frac{Z_1 Z_{0T}}{2} + \frac{Z_1 Z_2}{2} + Z_2 Z_{0T} = Z_2 Z_{0T} + \frac{Z_1 Z_{0T}}{2} + Z_{0T}^2$$

or
$$Z_1^2/4 + Z_1 Z_2 = Z_{0T}^2$$

or
$$Z_{0T} = \sqrt{Z_1 Z_2 + Z_1^2/4}$$

    Now let Z_{OC} and Z_{SC} be the open-circuit and short-circuit impedances of the network.

Hence
$$Z_{OC} = \frac{Z_1}{2} + Z_2$$

$$Z_{SC} = \frac{Z_1}{2} + \frac{Z_2 Z_1/2}{Z_2 + Z_1/2} = \frac{Z_1 Z_2 + Z_1^2/4}{Z_2 + Z_1/2}$$

Hence
$$Z_{OC}Z_{SC} = Z_1 Z_2 + Z_1^2/4$$

which equals Z_{OT}^2.

Therefore
$$Z_{OT} = \sqrt{Z_{OC}Z_{SC}}$$

Now from Section 3.2(a) we have

$$\cosh \gamma = 1 + \frac{Z_1}{2Z_2} = \frac{Z_2 + Z_1/2}{Z_2} = \frac{Z_{OC}}{Z_2} \qquad \text{from above}$$

Also
$$\sinh \gamma = \sqrt{\cosh^2 \gamma - 1}$$

$$= \sqrt{\left(1 + \frac{Z_1}{2Z_2}\right)^2 - 1}$$

$$= \sqrt{\frac{Z_1 Z_2 + Z_1^2/4}{Z_2^2}} = \frac{Z_{OT}}{Z_2}$$

Hence
$$\tanh \gamma = \frac{\sinh \gamma}{\cosh \gamma} = \frac{Z_{OT}}{Z_2}\frac{Z_2}{Z_{OC}} = \frac{Z_{OT}}{Z_{OC}} = \frac{\sqrt{Z_{OC}Z_{SC}}}{Z_{OC}}$$

or
$$\tanh \gamma = \sqrt{Z_{SC}/Z_{OC}}$$

Comment

To evaluate γ which is complex the following method is used.

Since $\gamma = \alpha + j\beta$, α and β being real quantities are evaluated from well-known trigonometric relationships given below.

Let $\tanh \gamma = \tanh(\alpha + j\beta) = A + jB$ since it is complex.

Hence
$$\tanh 2\alpha = \frac{2A}{1 + A^2 + B^2}$$

$$\tan 2\beta = \frac{2B}{1 - A^2 - B^2}$$

from which α and β are obtained using standard tables.

(c) π Network

Let $Z_{0\pi}$ be the characteristic impedance of the network in Fig. 3.6 which is correctly terminated.

Hence
$$Z_i = \frac{2Z_2 \left[Z_1 + \dfrac{2Z_2 Z_{0\pi}}{2Z_2 + Z_{0\pi}} \right]}{2Z_2 + Z_1 + \dfrac{2Z_2 Z_{0\pi}}{2Z_2 + Z_{0\pi}}}$$

which equals $Z_{0\pi}$ by definition.

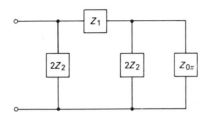

Fig. 3.6

Expanding the right-hand side and equating to $Z_{0\pi}$ gives

$$4Z_2^2 Z_1 + 2Z_2 Z_1 Z_{0\pi} + 4Z_2^2 Z_{0\pi} = 4Z_2^2 Z_{0\pi} + 2Z_2 Z_{0\pi}^2 + 2Z_1 Z_2 Z_{0\pi}$$
$$+ Z_1 Z_{0\pi}^2 + 2Z_2 Z_{0\pi}^2$$

or

$$\frac{4Z_1 Z_2^2}{4Z_2 + Z_1} = Z_{0\pi}^2$$

Hence

$$Z_{0\pi} = \frac{Z_1 Z_2}{\sqrt{(Z_1 Z_2 + Z_1^2)/4}} = \frac{Z_1 Z_2}{Z_{0T}}$$

Now let Z_{OC} and Z_{SC} be the open-circuit and short-circuit impedances respectively.

Here

$$Z_{OC} = \frac{2Z_2(Z_1 + 2Z_2)}{2Z_2 + Z_1 + 2Z_2}$$

$$= \frac{2Z_2(Z_1 + 2Z_2)}{Z_1 + 4Z_2}$$

and

$$Z_{SC} = \frac{2Z_2 Z_1}{(2Z_2 + Z_1)}$$

Therefore $\quad Z_{OC} Z_{SC} = \dfrac{2Z_2 \times 2Z_2 Z_1}{Z_1 + 4Z_2} = \dfrac{Z_1^2 Z_2^2}{Z_1 Z_2 + (Z_1^2/4)} = Z_{0\pi}^2$

or

$$Z_{0\pi} = \sqrt{Z_{OC} Z_{SC}}$$

Again, from Section 3.2(a) we have

$$\cosh \gamma = 1 + \frac{Z_1}{2Z_2} = \frac{2Z_2 + Z_1}{2Z_2} = \frac{Z_1}{Z_{SC}}$$

and

$$\sinh \gamma = \sqrt{\cosh^2 \gamma - 1}$$

$$= \sqrt{\frac{Z_1}{Z_2} + \frac{Z_1^2}{4Z_2^2}}$$

$$= \frac{\sqrt{Z_1 Z_2 + (Z_1^2/4)}}{Z_2} = \frac{Z_1}{Z_{0\pi}}$$

Therefore $$\tanh \gamma = \frac{\sinh \gamma}{\cosh \gamma}$$

$$= \frac{Z_1}{Z_{0\pi}} \times \frac{Z_{SC}}{Z_1} = \frac{Z_{SC}}{\sqrt{Z_{OC}Z_{SC}}}$$

or $$\tanh \gamma = \sqrt{\frac{Z_{SC}}{Z_{OC}}}$$

from which γ can be evaluated as for the T network.

Comments

1. $\cosh \gamma = 1 + (Z_1/2Z_2)$ for T, π or ladder networks.

2. $\tanh \gamma = \sqrt{\dfrac{Z_{SC}}{Z_{OC}}}$ for T or π networks.

3. $Z_{0T}Z_{0\pi} = Z_1 Z_2$.

Example 3.1

Deduce the relationships between the impedances of a symmetrical π network and those of the equivalent T network.

The circuit shown in Fig. 3.7 represents a particular π network. Determine from first principles the impedances of the equivalent T network for a frequency of 800 Hz.

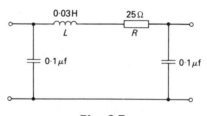

Fig. 3.7

If the resistance of one branch of the equivalent network is found to be negative, how can this effect be incorporated in the actual equivalent network.   (U.L.)

Solution

Let the respective impedances of a T network and a π network be as shown in Fig. 3.8.

For the two networks to be *equivalent*, impedances looking into corresponding terminals must be the same. Hence, looking into terminals (1) and (2) we have

for the T network   for the π network

$$(Z_A + Z_B) = \frac{Z_2(Z_1 + Z_2)}{Z_1 + 2Z_2}$$

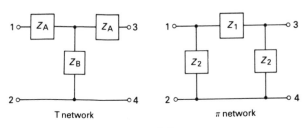

Fig. 3.8

Looking into terminals (1) and (3) we have

for the T network   for the π network

$$(Z_A + Z_A) = \frac{Z_1 2Z_2}{Z_1 + 2Z_2}$$

or

$$Z_A = \frac{Z_1 Z_2}{Z_1 + 2Z_2}$$

Substituting for Z_A in the equation for $(Z_A + Z_B)$ above yields

$$Z_B = \frac{Z_2^2}{Z_1 + 2Z_2}$$

Now $\quad Z_1 = 25 + j5000 \times 3 \times 10^{-2} = (25 + j150)\,\Omega$

$$Z_2 = -j\frac{1}{5000 \times 10^{-7}} = -j2000\,\Omega$$

Hence $\quad Z_A = \frac{(25 + j150)(-j2000)}{(25 + j150 - j4000)} = \frac{(1 + j6)2000}{154}\,\Omega$

$$= (13 + j78)\,\Omega$$

Hence $\quad R_A = 13\,\Omega$

$$L_A = \frac{78}{5000} = 15\!\cdot\!6 \text{ mH}$$

and $\quad Z_B = \frac{(-j2000)^2}{25(1 - j154)} = \frac{-4 \times 10^6 (1 + j154)}{25 \times 154 \times 154}$

or $\quad R_B - j\frac{1}{\omega C_B} = (-6\!\cdot\!75 - j1040)\,\Omega$

Hence $\quad R_B = -6\!\cdot\!75\,\Omega$

and $\quad C_B = \frac{1}{5000 \times 1040} = 0\!\cdot\!192\,\mu\text{F}$

The T network

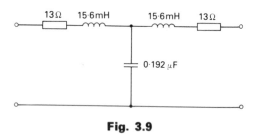

Fig. 3.9

Last part
If the resistance of one branch of the equivalent network is found to be negative, then this corresponds to power *generation*, since a positive resistance is associated with power *dissipation*. It can be incorporated in the branch by drawing a voltage generator in series with the resistance of that branch.

Example 3.2
Define the term *insertion loss* for a transmission network. Draw the diagram of a circuit for measuring, by comparison with a calibrated attenuator, the loss of a network inserted between equal resistive terminations.

Calculate the loss in dB of an *LC* network inserted between the source and load as shown in Fig. 3.10.   (U.L.)

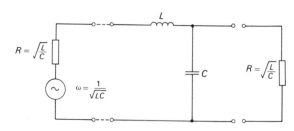

Fig. 3.10

When a network is inserted between a generator and load, the power loss in the load is called the insertion loss. Hence, If P_1 is the power in the load *without* the network inserted and P_2 is the power in the load *with* the network inserted, then the insertion loss is $10 \log P_1 / P_2$ dB.

To measure the insertion loss the circuit shown in Fig. 3.11 may be used, such that the network or the calibrated attenuator may be suitably switched into circuit separately, together with a power meter (or milliammeter) and the proper terminating load.

With the network inserted first, the generator voltage is adjusted to give a suitable value of power through the load or a suitable load current (if a milliammeter is used). The network is then switched out and the attenuator is switched in.

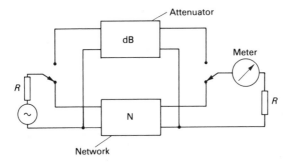

Fig. 3.11

The attenuator, which is usually calibrated in dB, is adjusted until the power meter (or milliammeter) reads the same value as for the previous measurement. The insertion loss is then read directly in dB from the attenuator setting (see Fig. 3.11).

Solution

(a) Without network

Let I_1 be the load current through the load $R = \sqrt{L/C}$ and the generator voltage V.

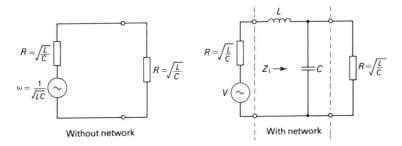

Fig. 3.12

Hence
$$|I_1| = \frac{V}{2R}$$

(b) With network

$$Z_i = j\omega L + \frac{(1/j\omega C)R}{(1/j\omega C) + R}$$

$$= j\omega L + \frac{R}{1 + j\omega CR}$$

Hence
$$I = \frac{V}{R + Z_i} = \frac{V}{(R + j\omega L) + R/(1 + j\omega CR)}$$

$$= \frac{V(1 + j\omega CR)}{(R + j\omega L)(1 + j\omega CR) + R}$$

and
$$I_2 = \left[\frac{1/j\omega C}{(1/j\omega C) + R} \right] I$$

$$= \frac{1}{(1 + j\omega CR)} \left[\frac{V(1 + j\omega CR)}{(R + j\omega L)(1 + j\omega CR) + R} \right]$$

$$= \frac{V}{R + j\omega L + j\omega CR^2 - \omega^2 LCR + R}$$

Since $\omega = 1/\sqrt{LC}$ and $R = \sqrt{L/C}$ this gives

$$I_2 = \frac{V}{R + jR + jR - R + R} = \frac{V}{R(1 + 2j)}$$

and
$$|I_2| = \frac{V}{R\sqrt{5}}$$

The insertion loss $= 20 \log_{10} \left| \frac{I_1}{I_2} \right|$

$$= 20 \log_{10} \frac{V}{2R} \frac{R\sqrt{5}}{V}$$

$$= 10 \log_{10} \tfrac{5}{4}$$

$$= 10 \log_{10} 1 \cdot 25$$

or insertion loss $= 0 \cdot 969$ dB

(d) Lattice network

Let its characteristic impedance equal Z_0 where $Z_0 = \sqrt{Z_{OC} Z_{SC}}$.
From the equivalent circuit we have

$$Z_{OC} = \frac{Z_1 + Z_2}{2}$$

$$Z_{SC} = \frac{2Z_1 Z_2}{Z_1 + Z_2}$$

Hence
$$Z_0^2 = Z_1 Z_2$$

or
$$Z_0 = \sqrt{Z_1 Z_2}$$

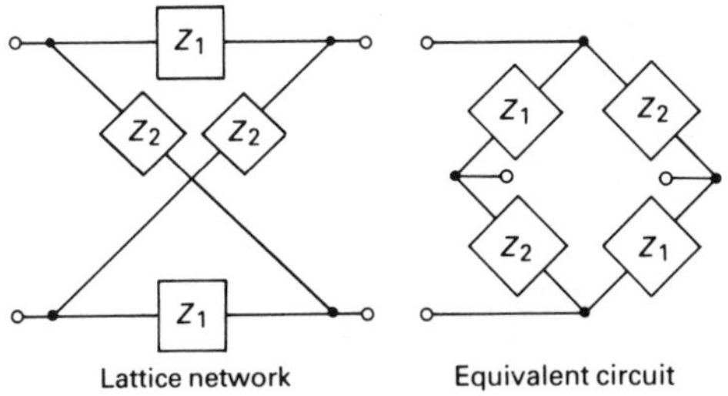
Z_1
Z_2
Z_2
Z_1
Lattice network
Z_1
Z_2
Z_2
Z_1
Equivalent circuit

Fig. 3.13

Now
$$\tanh \gamma = \sqrt{\frac{Z_{SC}}{Z_{OC}}}$$
$$= \frac{2\sqrt{Z_1 Z_2}}{Z_1 + Z_2}$$
$$= \frac{2Z_1 Z_0}{Z_1^2 + Z_0^2}$$

or
$$\frac{e^{2\gamma} - 1}{e^{2\gamma} + 1} = \frac{2Z_1 Z_0}{Z_1^2 + Z_0^2}$$

Hence we obtain
$$e^{2\gamma} = \frac{(Z_0 + Z_1)^2}{(Z_0 - Z_1)^2}$$

or
$$e^{\gamma} = \frac{Z_0 + Z_1}{Z_0 - Z_1} \qquad \text{(using the positive value)}$$

Now
$$\tanh \frac{\gamma}{2} = \frac{e^{\gamma} - 1}{e^{\gamma} + 1}$$

Hence
$$\tanh \frac{\gamma}{2} = \frac{2Z_1}{2Z_0} = \frac{Z_1}{Z_0} = \sqrt{\frac{Z_1}{Z_2}}$$

(e) Bridged T network

Let Z_0 be the characteristic impedance of the network in Fig. 3.14 where
$$Z_0 = \sqrt{Z_{OC} Z_{SC}}$$

Here
$$Z_{OC} = \frac{\frac{Z_1}{2}\left(Z_3 + \frac{Z_1}{2}\right)}{\frac{Z_1}{2} + Z_3 + \frac{Z_1}{2}} + Z_2$$

$$= \frac{Z_1 Z_2 + Z_2 Z_3 + \frac{Z_1^2}{4} + \frac{Z_1 Z_3}{2}}{Z_1 + Z_3}$$

and
$$Z_{SC} = \frac{Z_3\left[\dfrac{Z_1}{2} + \dfrac{Z_2(Z_1/2)}{Z_2 + (Z_1/2)}\right]}{Z_3 + \dfrac{Z_1}{2} + \dfrac{Z_2(Z_1/2)}{Z_2 + (Z_1/2)}}$$

$$= \frac{Z_3 \dfrac{Z_1^2}{4} + Z_3 Z_2 Z_1}{Z_3 \dfrac{Z_1}{2} + Z_2 Z_3 + \dfrac{Z_1^2}{4} + Z_1 Z_2}$$

Hence
$$Z_0 = \sqrt{\frac{\dfrac{Z_1^2 Z_3}{4} + Z_1 Z_2 Z_3}{Z_1 + Z_3}} = \sqrt{\left(\frac{Z_1^2}{4} + Z_1 Z_2\right)\frac{Z_3}{(Z_1 + Z_3)}}$$

Usually
$$\frac{Z_1}{2} = \sqrt{Z_2 Z_3}$$

Hence
$$Z_0 = \sqrt{Z_2(Z_1 + Z_3)\frac{Z_3}{Z_1 + Z_3}}$$

or
$$Z_0 = \sqrt{Z_2 Z_3}$$

and
$$\frac{Z_1}{2} = \sqrt{Z_2 Z_3} = Z_0 \text{ also}$$

Now assume the network is terminated in Z_0 and rearranged as in Fig. 3.14. A voltage V_s is applied to it and for the currents shown we obtain for branches AC and CD

$$I_3 Z_3 + I_R Z_0 = V_s = I_s Z_0$$

and for branches AB, BC and CD

$$I_s \frac{Z_1}{2} - I_3 Z_1 + I_R\left(\frac{Z_1}{2} + Z_0\right) = V_s = I_s Z_0$$

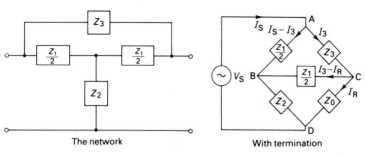

The network   With termination

Fig. 3.14

Eliminating I_3 between these equations yields

$$I_R = \frac{I_S Z_0(Z_1 + Z_3) - I_S \dfrac{Z_1 Z_3}{2}}{Z_0 Z_1 + \dfrac{Z_1 Z_3}{2} + Z_3 Z_0}$$

$$= \frac{I_S \left[Z_0(Z_1 + Z_3) - \dfrac{Z_1 Z_3}{2} \right]}{Z_0(Z_1 + Z_3) + \dfrac{Z_1 Z_3}{2}}$$

or

$$\frac{I_S}{I_R} = \frac{Z_0(Z_1 + Z_3) + \dfrac{Z_1 Z_3}{2}}{Z_0(Z_1 + Z_3) - \dfrac{Z_1 Z_3}{2}}$$

Since $Z_1/2 = Z_0$ we obtain

$$\frac{I_S}{I_R} = \frac{Z_1 + 2Z_3}{Z_1} = 1 + \frac{Z_3}{Z_0}$$

or

$$\gamma = \log_e \frac{I_S}{I_R} = \log_e \left(1 + \frac{Z_3}{Z_0} \right)$$

But $Z_0 = \sqrt{Z_2 Z_3}$ and so alternatively

$$\gamma = \log_e \left(1 + \frac{Z_0}{Z_2} \right)$$

from which γ may be evaluated.

(f)   Twin-T network[17]

The general form of an *RC* twin-T network is shown in Fig. 3.15(a). It can be regarded as a parallel arrangement of a low-pass T network consisting of R_1, R_2 and C_3 together with a high-pass T network consisting of C_1, C_2 and R_3. By proper design, the twin-T network can be made to function as a band-stop filter or 'notch' filter. A typical structure used for this purpose is shown in Fig. 3.15(b).

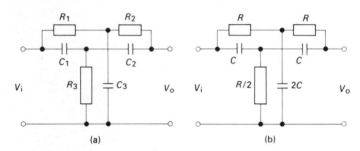

Fig. 3.15

In Appendix B it is shown that the conditions for zero transmission through the network which yields $V_o = 0$ for a finite value of input voltage V_i at a given frequency ω_o are given by

$$\omega_o^2 = \frac{(C_1 + C_2)}{R_1 R_2 C_1 C_2 C_3}$$

and

$$\omega_o^2 = \frac{1}{C_1 C_2 R_3 (R_1 + R_2)}$$

In practice, we usually make $R_1 = R_2 = R$ and $R_3 = R/2$ while $C_1 = C_2 = C$ and $C_3 = 2C$. In this case, the notch frequency ω_o is given by

$$\omega_o = \frac{1}{RC}$$

or

$$f_o = \frac{1}{2\pi RC}$$

and the structure can be used for suppressing an interfering signal at the notch frequency f_o. A typical application of this is in a monochrome television receiver for removing the colour sub-carrier at a frequency of about 4·43 MHz, prior to demodulation.

3.3   Asymmetrical networks

These are networks whose input and output ports are dissimilar and hence cannot be interchanged.

(a) Iterative impedances

The input impedances at the two ends of such a network are different and are called the iterative impedances. This is illustrated in Fig. 3.16 where it is assumed that Z_1 and Z_2 are the two iterative impedances.

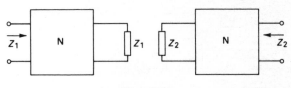

Fig. 3.16

(b) Image impedances

An asymmetrical network has two different image impedances also, such that when one of them terminates the network the other is seen at the input terminals and vice versa. This is illustrated in Fig. 3.18 where it is assumed that Z_A and Z_B are the two image impedances.

Comments
1. Networks when used in series with one another are connected on an *iterative* basis for matching purposes.
2. Networks which are purely resistive are connected on an *image* basis when used for the maximum transfer of power between generator and load.
3. In the case of *symmetrical* networks, the two iterative impedances and the two image impedances are all equal to one another and called simply the *characteristic impedance*.

(c) The half-section

An asymmetrical network of particular importance is the L section or half-section. It is obtained by dividing a T section or π section into two. Either half constitutes an L section as shown in Fig. 3.17.

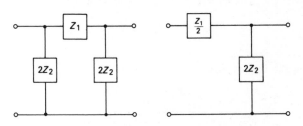

Fig. 3.17

Such an L section has two iterative impedances and two image impedances. The image impedances have a special significance for matching purposes as is shown subsequently (Fig. 3.18).

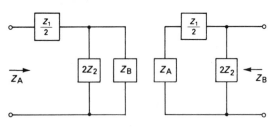

Fig. 3.18

Image impedances
Let Z_A and Z_B be the image impedances as shown in Fig. 3.18.

We have
$$Z_A = \frac{Z_1}{2} + \frac{2Z_2 Z_B}{2Z_2 + Z_B}$$

Hence
$$2Z_A Z_2 + Z_A Z_B - Z_1 Z_2 - \frac{Z_1 Z_B}{2} - 2Z_2 Z_B = 0$$

or
$$Z_A Z_B + 2Z_A Z_2 - (\tfrac{1}{2}Z_1 + 2Z_2)Z_B = Z_1 Z_2$$

Again
$$Z_B = \frac{2Z_2[(Z_1/2) + Z_A]}{2Z_2 + (Z_1/2) + Z_A}$$

Hence
$$2Z_2 Z_B + \frac{Z_1 Z_B}{2} + Z_A Z_B = Z_1 Z_2 + 2Z_2 Z_A$$

or
$$Z_A Z_B - 2Z_A Z_2 + \left(\frac{Z_1}{2} + 2Z_2\right)Z_B = Z_1 Z_2$$

Subtracting this expression from the previous one for $Z_1 Z_2$ also yields

$$4Z_A Z_2 - 2\left(\frac{Z_1}{2} + 2Z_2\right)Z_B = 0$$

or
$$\frac{Z_A}{Z_B} = \frac{(Z_1/4) + Z_2}{Z_2} \tag{1}$$

Adding the two expressions for $Z_1 Z_2$ gives

$$Z_A Z_B = Z_1 Z_2 \tag{2}$$

Hence
$$\frac{Z_A}{Z_B}(Z_A Z_B) = \frac{(Z_1/4) + Z_2}{Z_2}(Z_1 Z_2) = \frac{Z_1^2}{4} + Z_1 Z_2$$

or $Z_A = \sqrt{Z_1 Z_2 + (Z_1^2/4)} = Z_{0T}$ from Section 3.2(b). Similarly by division of (2) by (1) we have

$$\frac{Z_A Z_B}{Z_A/Z_B} = \frac{Z_1 Z_2 \times Z_2}{[(Z_1/4) + Z_2]} = \frac{Z_1^2 Z_2^2}{(Z_1^2/4) + Z_1 Z_2}$$

or $Z_B = Z_1 Z_2 / Z_{0T} = Z_{0\pi}$ from Section 3.2(c).

Comments
1. The image impedances at the two ends of an L section are equal to the characteristic impedances of a T or π full-section respectively. Hence they can be used for matching a T network to a π network.
2. The general formula $Z_0 = \sqrt{Z_{OC} Z_{SC}}$ applies to the two *image* impedances and can be used to determine them. It *does not* hold good for the two *iterative* impedances, which must be determined from first principles.

(d) Image transfer coefficient, θ
This is defined as one half of the Naperian logarithm of complex ratio of the volt-amps entering and leaving the network when it is terminated in its image impedances.

$$\theta = \tfrac{1}{2} \log_e \frac{V_S I_S}{V_R I_R}$$

where V_S, I_S refer to the input voltage and current and V_R, I_R refer to the output voltage and current respectively.

Since θ is complex, it may likewise be expressed as $\theta = \alpha + j\beta$ where α is the image attenuation coefficient and β is the image phase-change coefficient.

Example 3.3
Define the terms image impedance Z_I and image transfer coefficient γ as applied to linear passive two-terminal-pair networks.

Show that, if R_1, R_2 and R in Fig. 3.19 are related by $R_1 R_2 = R^2$, then

$$Z_I = R \text{ and } e^\gamma = 1 + \frac{R_1}{R}$$

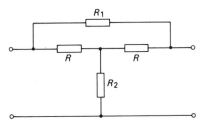

Fig. 3.19

The following may be used without proof:

$$Z_I^2 = Z_{OC} Z_{SC}$$

and
$$\tanh \gamma = \frac{e^{2\gamma} - 1}{e^{2\gamma} + 1} = \sqrt{\frac{Z_{SC}}{Z_{OC}}}$$

where Z_{OC} is the open-circuit driving-point impedance and Z_{SC} is the short-circuit driving-point impedance.   (U.L.)

Solution
The image impedances of an asymmetrical network are the two different impedances at the ends of the network and are such that when one impedance terminates the network the other is seen at the input terminals and vice versa.

The image transfer coefficient γ is defined as one half of the Naperian logarithm of the ratio of input volt-amps over the output volt-amps, when the network is terminated at either end in its image impedances.

Since
$$Z_I^2 = Z_{OC} \times Z_{SC}$$

Hence

$$Z_{OC} = R_2 + \frac{R(R_1 + R)}{(2R + R_1)} = \frac{2RR_2 + R_1 R + 2R^2}{2R + R_1} \quad \text{(since } R_1 R_2 = R^2 \text{)}$$

and

$$Z_{SC} = \frac{[R + (RR_2/R + R_2)]R_1}{[R + (RR_2/R + R_2)] + R_1} = \frac{R^2 R_1 + 2RR_1 R_2}{R^2 + 2RR_2 + RR_1 + R_1 R_2}$$

$$= \frac{R_1 R^2 + 2R^3}{2R^2 + 2RR_2 + RR_1}$$

Hence

$$Z_I^2 = Z_{OC} \times Z_{SC} = \frac{(2RR_2 + RR_1 + 2R^2)}{2R + R_1} \times \frac{R_1 R + 2R^3}{(2R^2 + 2RR_2 + RR_1)}$$

$$= \frac{R^2(2R + R_1)}{2R + R_1} = R^2$$

or

$$Z_I = R$$

Again

$$\tanh \gamma = \frac{e^{2\gamma} - 1}{e^{2\gamma} + 1}$$

$$= \sqrt{\frac{R_1 R^2 + 2R^3}{(2R^2 + 2RR_2 + RR_1)} \times \frac{2R + R_1}{(2RR_2 + RR_1 + 2R^2)}}$$

$$= \frac{(2R + R_1)}{(2R + R_1) + 2R_2}$$

Hence, we obtain

$$\frac{2e^{2\gamma}}{-2} = \frac{2(2R+R_1)+2R_2}{-2R_2}$$

or

$$e^{2\gamma} = \frac{(2R+R_1)+R_2}{R_2}$$

$$= 1 + \frac{2R+R_1}{R_2}$$

Now

$$R_1 R_2 = R^2$$

$$e^{2\gamma} = 1 + \frac{2R+R_1}{R^2/R_1}$$

$$= 1 + \frac{2RR_1+R_1^2}{R^2}$$

$$= \left(\frac{R+R_1}{R}\right)^2$$

with

$$e^{\gamma} = \frac{R+R_1}{R}$$

or

$$e^{\gamma} = 1 + \frac{R_1}{R}$$

Example 3.4
Explain what is meant by the term asymmetrical when applied to two-port networks. An unbalanced two-port resistive network has input terminals 1 and 2 and output terminals 3 and 4. The values of resistance measured at 1–2 when terminals 3–4 are first short-circuited and then open-circuited are respectively 275 Ω and 500 Ω. The resistance measured at 3–4 with 1–2 open-circuited is 400 Ω. Determine the equivalent T network and the image impedances. Hence calculate the insertion loss produced by the network when inserted between its image impedances. (U.L.)

Solution
An asymmetrical network is one whose input and output ports are dissimilar and therefore are not interchangeable.
Let the network consist of resistors R_1, R_2 and R_3 as shown in Fig. 3.20.

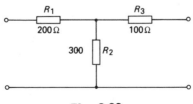

Fig. 3.20

From the data given we have

$$R_1 + R_2 = 500 \tag{1}$$

$$R_1 + \frac{R_2 R_3}{R_2 + R_3} = 275 \tag{2}$$

$$R_2 + R_3 = 400 \tag{3}$$

From (2) and (3)

$$R_1 + \frac{R_2 R_3}{400} = 275 \tag{4}$$

From (1)

$$R_2 = 500 - R_1 \tag{5}$$

From (1) and (3)

$$R_1 - R_3 = 100 \tag{6}$$

From (4), (5) and (6)

$$R_1 + \frac{(500 - R_1)(R_1 - 100)}{400} = 275$$

or $\qquad 400R_1 + 500R_1 - R_1^2 - 50\,000 + 100R_1 = 110\,000$

Hence $\qquad R_1^2 - 1000R_1 + 160\,000 = 0$

or $\qquad (R_1 - 800)(R_1 - 200) = 0$

Therefore $\qquad R_1 = 800\,\Omega \quad \text{or} \quad 200\,\Omega$

$$R_2 = (500 - 800)\,\Omega \quad \text{or} \quad (500 - 200)\,\Omega$$

Hence $\qquad R_2 = 300\,\Omega$

and $\qquad R_1 = 200\,\Omega \qquad (R_1 = 800\,\Omega \text{ inadmissible})$

$$R_3 = 400 - R_2 = 100\,\Omega$$

The image impedances Z_A and Z_B are obtained from the expression $Z_0 = \sqrt{Z_{OC} Z_{SC}}$ applied at the respective ends.

For Z_A $\qquad\qquad Z_{OC} = 500\,\Omega$

$$Z_{SC} = 200 + \frac{300 \times 100}{400} = 275\,\Omega$$

or $\qquad\qquad\qquad Z_A = \sqrt{500 \times 275} = 371\,\Omega$

For Z_B $\qquad\qquad Z_{OC} = 400\,\Omega$

$$Z_{SC} = 100 + \frac{300 \times 200}{500} = 220\,\Omega$$

$$Z_B = \sqrt{400 \times 220} = 297\,\Omega$$

Insertion loss Since the terminating impedances are the image impedances, the input generator impedance is $371\,\Omega$ and the terminating or load impedance is $297\,\Omega$. *Without the network* Let the generator voltage be V and the current through the load I_1.

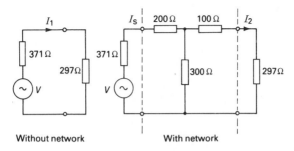

Fig. 3.21

Hence
$$I_1 = \frac{V}{371 + 297} = \frac{V}{668}$$

With the network   Let the input current to the network be I_s and the load current be I_2 for a generator voltage V.

Hence
$$I_s = \frac{V}{371 + 371} = \frac{V}{742}$$

Also
$$I_2 = \left[\frac{300}{300 + 100 + 297}\right] I_s = \frac{300\,V}{697 \times 742}$$

The insertion loss $= 20 \log \dfrac{I_1}{I_2}$

$$= 20 \log \frac{V}{668} \times \frac{697 \times 742}{300\,V}$$

$$= 20 \log(2 \cdot 58)$$

$$= 8 \cdot 232 \text{ dB}$$

3.4   Network parameters[18, 19]

An analysis of the properties of a linear two-port network can be undertaken through the use of various sets of parameters relating the input and output voltages and currents v_1, i_1 and v_2, i_2 respectively. Each set of parameters may be determined by either open-circuit or short-circuit measurements on the network, where the positive directions of voltages and currents are as shown in Fig. 3.22.

For approximately linear operation, any parameter z can be expressed as a function of two other parameters x and y in the form $z = f(x, y)$. Hence, an incremental change dz is related to changes in x and y by the relationship

$$dz = \frac{\partial z}{\partial x}\,dx + \frac{\partial z}{\partial y}\,dy$$

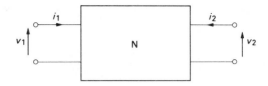

Fig. 3.22

and for small signal changes (d.c. or a.c.), the partial derivatives assume constant values. This is the basic equation relating the various sets of parameters and for convenience small letters are used to indicate voltage or current changes in all cases.

(a) $ABCD$ parameters
The input voltage and current are given in terms of the output voltage and current. If the load current i_2 is negative when it flows *outwards* into a load, we obtain the basic equations

$$v_1 = Av_2 - Bi_2$$
$$i_1 = Cv_2 - Di_2$$

where

$$A = v_1/v_2 \quad \text{with } i_2 = 0$$
$$B = -v_1/i_2 \quad \text{with } v_2 = 0$$
$$C = i_1/v_2 \quad \text{with } i_2 = 0$$
$$D = -i_1/i_2 \quad \text{with } v_2 = 0$$

Hence, the parameters can be determined by means of open-circuit and short-circuit measurements on the network. Furthermore, A and D are pure numbers while B is an impedance and C is an admittance.

(b) z parameters
If the input and output voltages are expressed in terms of the input and output currents, it leads to the impedance or z parameters of the network. Hence, we obtain

$$v_1 = z_{11}i_1 + z_{12}i_2$$
$$v_2 = z_{21}i_1 + z_{22}i_2$$

where

$$z_{11} = v_1/i_1 \quad \text{with } i_2 = 0$$
$$z_{12} = v_1/i_2 \quad \text{with } i_1 = 0$$
$$z_{21} = v_2/i_1 \quad \text{with } i_2 = 0$$
$$z_{22} = v_2/i_2 \quad \text{with } i_1 = 0$$

Since the impedances are derived under open-circuit conditions i.e. $i_1 = 0$ or $i_2 = 0$, the z parameters are also called the open-circuit impedance parameters. Furthermore, in certain applications it is convenient to express the impedances in terms of the input and output subscripts i and o respectively or with the forward and reverse subscripts f and r respectively. Thus, we have

$$z_{11} = z_i = \text{input impedance}$$
$$z_{12} = z_f = \text{forward transfer impedance}$$
$$z_{21} = z_r = \text{reverse transfer impedance}$$
$$z_{22} = z_o = \text{output impedance}$$

with
$$v_i = z_i i_i + z_f i_o$$
$$v_o = z_r i_i + z_o i_o$$

(c) y parameters

If the input and output currents are expressed in terms of the input and output voltages, it leads to the *admittance* or y parameters of the network. For input and output currents i_1 and i_2 respectively, the two-port network equations are

$$i_1 = y_{11} v_1 + y_{12} v_2$$
$$i_2 = y_{21} v_1 + y_{22} v_2$$

If the output terminals are short-circuited so that $v_2 = 0$ then

$$y_{11} = i_1/v_1 = y_i = \text{input admittance}$$
$$y_{21} = i_2/v_1 = y_f = \text{forward transfer admittance}$$

and if instead, the input terminals are short-circuited so that $v_1 = 0$, then

$$y_{12} = i_1/v_2 = y_r = \text{reverse transfer admittance}$$
$$y_{22} = i_2/v_2 = y_o = \text{output admittance}$$

Hence, y_i, y_f, y_r and y_o are the small signal parameters which are also known as the short-circuit admittance parameters, since they can be determined by short-circuit measurements on the two-port network. The parameters are usefully applied to field-effect transistor circuits such as those for the JFET and MOSFET, and particularly with high-frequency operation.

(d) h parameters

In this case, the input voltage and output current are related to the input current and output voltage. It yields the 'hybrid' or h parameters which are so-called, because they may represent an impedance, admittance or a pure number. The basic network equations are

$$v_1 = h_{11}i_1 + h_{12}v_2$$
$$i_2 = h_{21}i_1 + h_{22}v_2$$

If the output terminals are short-circuited so that $v_2 = 0$, then

$$h_{11} = v_1/i_1 = h_i = \text{input impedance}$$
$$h_{21} = i_2/i_1 = h_f = \text{forward current gain}$$

and if the input terminals are open-circuited so that $i_1 = 0$, then

$$h_{12} = v_1/v_2 = h_r = \text{reverse voltage gain}$$
$$h_{22} = i_2/v_2 = h_o = \text{output admittance}$$

The parameters are extensively used in the small-signal analysis of bipolar transistors and are defined according to the various configurations known as common-emitter, common-base and common-collector by the use of an additional subscript. For example, the parameter h_i is designated as h_{ie}, h_{ib} or h_{ic} when used in the respective configurations mentioned above.

(e) *g* parameters
By expressing the input current and output voltage in terms of the input voltage and output current of the network, we obtain the *g parameters*. Hence, we have

$$i_1 = g_{11}v_1 + g_{12}i_2$$
$$v_2 = g_{21}v_1 + g_{22}i_2$$

If the output terminals are open-circuited so that $i_2 = 0$, then

$$g_{11} = i_1/v_1 = \text{input admittance}$$
$$g_{21} = v_2/v_1 = \text{forward voltage gain}$$

and if the input terminals are short-circuited so that $v_1 = 0$, then

$$g_{12} = i_1/i_2 = \text{inverse current gain}$$
$$g_{22} = v_2/i_2 = \text{output impedance}$$

The *g* parameters are also called the inverse *h* parameters because of their inverse relationship with the latter. Thus, we obtain

$$g_{11} = 1/h_{11} \qquad g_{22} = 1/h_{22}$$
$$g_{12} = 1/h_{21} \qquad g_{21} = 1/h_{12}$$

(f) *s* parameters[20]
An alternative way of describing the behaviour of a network is in terms of incident and reflected waves rather than by voltages and currents, since the

former are, in practice, more easily measured, as, for example, in the case of microwave networks. Here, the behaviour of the network is more conveniently described in terms of the *scattering* or *s* parameters which can be succinctly expressed in the form of a *scattering matrix S* relating the incident and output waves of the network.

A typical example is the two-port network shown in Fig. 3.23 where a_i is the incident wave, b_i is the reflected wave at the input port. Similarly, a_o is the incident wave and b_o is the reflected wave at the output port. Hence, we have

$$b_i = s_{11}a_i + s_{12}a_o$$
$$b_o = s_{21}a_i + s_{22}a_o$$

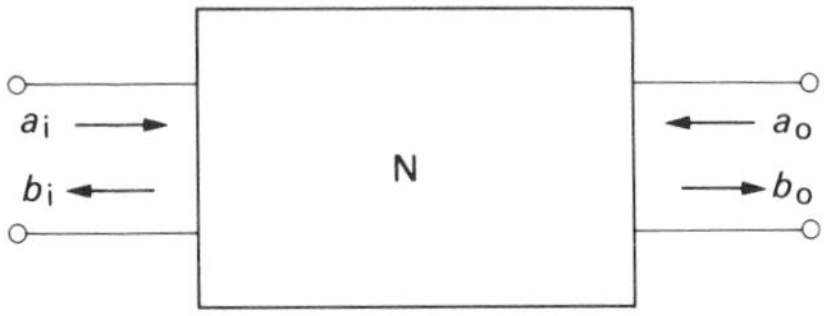

Fig. 3.23

When $z_i = z_L = z_o$ is the characteristic impedance of the network, we obtain the *s* parameters given by

$$s_{11} = b_i/a_i = \text{input reflection coefficient}$$
$$s_{12} = b_i/a_o = \text{reverse transmission gain}$$
$$s_{21} = b_o/a_i = \text{forward transmission gain}$$
$$s_{22} = b_o/a_o = \text{output reflection coefficient}$$

For a general incident wave a and scattered wave b, the two-port scattering matrix S is expressed in the form

$$S = \begin{vmatrix} s_{11} & s_{12} \\ s_{21} & s_{22} \end{vmatrix}$$

where the waves a and b have the dimensions of power with $b = Sa$.

Example 3.5
With the aid of the reciprocity theorem show that an important relationship between the $ABCD$ parameters for a two-port network is given by $AD - BC = 1$.

Solution
If a voltage v is applied alternately to the input and output terminals of the network, which is short-circuited at one end, let the input and output currents be as shown in Fig. 3.24.

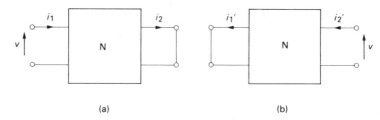

Fig. 3.24

From the basic equations we obtain from Fig. 3.24(a)

$$v = A \times 0 - Bi_2 = -Bi_2 \tag{1}$$

$$i_1 = C \times 0 - Di_2 = -Di_2 \tag{2}$$

and from Fig. 3.24(b)

$$0 = Av + Bi'_2 \tag{3}$$

$$-i'_1 = Cv + Di'_2 \tag{4}$$

Thus, from equations (3) and (4) we obtain

$$i'_2 = -(A/B)v$$

$$-i'_1 = Cv + D(-A/B)v = \left(\frac{BC - AD}{B} \right)v$$

and substituting for $v/B = -i_2$ from equation (1) yields

$$-i'_1 = (AD - BC)i_2$$

Now, from the reciprocity theorem, the short-circuit currents at the output and input of the network are equal i.e. $i_2 = -i'_1$ and so we obtain $(AD - BC) = 1$ which is the required relationship.

Example 3.6
Define the $ABCD$ parameters of a two-port network and give two relationships between them for a passive, linear, symmetrical network.

Fig. 3.25(a) shows a symmetrical lattice two-port network. Determine

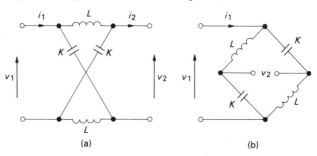

Fig. 3.25

(a) the $ABCD$ parameters in terms of θ and Z_0 where

$$\theta = \arccos\left[(1 - \omega^2 LK)/(1 + \omega^2 LK)\right] \text{ and } Z_0 = \sqrt{LK}$$

(b) the output/input voltage ratio $|V_2/V_1|$ with the network terminated in a resistance Z_0. (C.E.I.)

Solution
The answer to the first part of the question will be found in Section 3.4(a).

Problem
(a) The symmetrical lattice is redrawn in Fig. 3.25(b) as a bridge arrangement. With $i_2 = 0$ we have on open-circuit

$$v_1 = Av_2 \tag{1}$$

$$i_1 = Cv_2 \tag{2}$$

with
$$v_1/i_1 = Z_{OC} = A/C \tag{3}$$

and
$$Z_{OC} = \frac{j\omega L + 1/j\omega K}{2} = \frac{1 - \omega^2 LK}{2j\omega K} \tag{4}$$

With $v_2 = 0$ we have on short-circuit

$$v_1 = -Bi_2$$

$$i_2 = -Di_2$$

with
$$v_1/i_1 = Z_{SC} = B/D \tag{5}$$

and
$$Z_{SC} = 2\left[\frac{j\omega L \cdot 1/j\omega K}{j\omega L + 1/j\omega K}\right] = \frac{2j\omega L}{(1 - \omega^2 LK)} \tag{6}$$

Now
$$\cos\theta = \frac{1 - \omega^2 LK}{1 + \omega^2 LK}$$

or
$$\frac{1 - \cos\theta}{1 + \cos\theta} = \omega^2 LK$$

and
$$\tan^2 \theta/2 = \omega^2 LK \tag{7}$$

or
$$\tan \theta/2 = \omega\sqrt{LK} \tag{8}$$

Also, since $Z_0^2 = L/K$, substituting into equation (7) yields

$$\tan^2 \theta/2 = \omega^2 L^2/Z_0^2$$

or
$$\tan \theta/2 = \omega L/Z_0 = \omega K Z_0 \tag{9}$$

and from equations (4), (6), (7) and (9) we obtain

$$Z_{OC} = \frac{(1 - \tan^2 \theta/2)Z_0}{2j \tan \theta/2} = -jZ_0 \cot\theta \tag{10}$$

and
$$Z_{SC} = \frac{2jZ_0 \tan \theta/2}{1 - \tan^2 \theta/2} = jZ_0 \tan\theta \tag{11}$$

Now from Fig. 3.25(b) we have

$$v_2 = \frac{i_1}{2}[j\omega L - 1/j\omega K] = -\frac{v_1}{2Z_{OC}}\left[\frac{1+\omega^2 LK}{j\omega K}\right]$$

and from equations (7), (9) and (10) we obtain

$$\frac{v_1}{v_2} = \frac{-2(-jZ_0\cot\theta)(j\tan\theta/2)}{Z_0(1+\tan^2\theta/2)} = -\cos\theta$$

with
$$A = v_1/v_2 = -\cos\theta \tag{12}$$

Since the network is symmetrical it follows that $A = D$. Hence

$$D = -\cos\theta \tag{13}$$

and from equations (5) and (11)

$$B = (-\cos\theta)(jZ_0\tan\theta) = -jZ_0\sin\theta$$

Also, from equations (3), (10) and (12) we obtain

$$C = \frac{A}{Z_{OC}} = \frac{-\cos\theta}{-jZ_0\cot\theta} = -\frac{j}{Z_0}\sin\theta \tag{14}$$

Hence

$$A = -\cos\theta$$

$$B = -jZ_0\sin\theta$$

$$C = -\frac{j}{Z_0}\sin\theta$$

$$D = -\cos\theta$$

(b)   The network can be regarded as a short, lossless transmission line which is correctly terminated in its characteristic resistance Z_0. Hence, the input and output voltages are equal in magnitude and we obtain

$$\left|\frac{v_2}{v_1}\right| = 1$$

4
Modern filter theory

4.1 Introduction

In the past, filters have been designed on the image-parameter basis as briefly described in Appendix C. More recently, however, due to the advent of the computer, which can undertake tedious calculations, filter design is based on the insertion-loss or synthesis approach. The essential difference is that in the older theory, a filter was designed according to the theory and its characteristics were accepted as final. In the modern approach, the filter is built up or synthesized bit by bit to give the required characteristics as nearly as possible.

This modern method is far more powerful and flexible than the older classical theory. The modern design procedure is to synthesize the filter from its voltage transfer function as nearly as possible, through the use of *approximation theory*[21]. In order to build a practical filter, only certain types of functions are physically realizable and are known as rational functions. The type of filter designed depends on the rational function chosen.

The three most common types of filters are the Butterworth, Chebyshev and elliptic function filters. The procedure is to choose one of the realizable rational functions and to obtain the required transfer function from the given amplitude or phase characteristic. The transfer function is then divided into various parts and the filter synthesized according to each part.

4.2 Design procedure

If $V_1(s)$ and $V_2(s)$ are the voltages at the input and output of the filter, then the voltage transfer function $H(s)$ which is considered to have only poles is given by

$$H(s) = \frac{V_2(s)}{V_1(s)} = \frac{1}{(s + s_1)(s + s_2) \ldots}$$

where $s = j\omega$ and s_1, s_2 etc. are the required poles.

In an ideal low-pass filter, for example, the ideal response would be unity over the pass band and would fall to zero at the cut-off frequency f_c. Such a characteristic could never be obtained in practice but may be approximated by various functions whose behaviour is best examined in terms of its poles.

The basic procedure is to choose the appropriate $H(s)$ and from it obtain the conjugate $H(-s)$. Multiplication of these functions yields $|H(s)|^2$ which involves the square of the amplitude only and its poles are then determined. Since the physical function is $H(s)$, only poles in the left half plane are considered in the design. This then enables $H(s)$ to be synthesized as a network.

Such filters do not possess a definite cut-off frequency as in classical theory, but are usually 'normalized' at the convenient value of $\omega_c = 1$, which is specified by the designer. Butterworth filters are usually normalized at the 3 dB point, and in the Chebyshev filter, this is taken as the last point of interest in the pass band. The analysis is best illustrated using the following designs.

4.3 Butterworth filter[22-24]

The Butterworth approximation of the ideal low-pass filter response is shown in Fig. 4.1 and given by

$$H_n(s) \cdot H_n(-s) = |H_n(s)|^2 = \frac{1}{1+\omega^{2n}} = \frac{1}{1+(s/j)^{2n}}$$

where $n = 1, 2, 3$ etc. and gives the order of the filter.

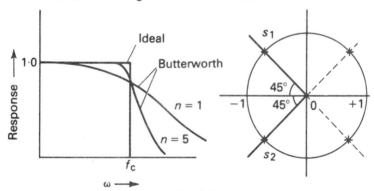

Fig. 4.1

The poles are given by $(s/j)^{2n} + 1 = 0$

i.e.
$$\left(\frac{s}{j}\right)^{2n} = -1$$

or
$$(-1)^{-n} \cdot s^{2n} = -1 = e^{j(2k-1)\pi}$$

where $k = 1, 2$ etc. . . . .

Hence
$$s^{2n} = e^{j(2k+n-1)\pi}$$

or
$$s_k = e^{j[(2k+n-1)/2n]\pi}$$

and the various poles are s_1, s_2 etc. . . . .

Hence $$H(s) = \frac{1}{(s+s_1)(s+s_2)\ldots}$$

As an example, assume $n = 2$ and we have

$$s^4 = -1 = 1\underline{/180}$$

or $$s^2 = \pm 1\underline{/90} = 1\underline{/\pm 90}$$

and $$s = \pm 1\underline{/\pm 45}$$

i.e. the required poles lie on a unit circle in the left-half plane at $\underline{/s} \pm 45°$ as shown in Fig. 4.1.

$$H(s) = \frac{1}{(s+1\underline{/45})(s+1\underline{/-45})}$$

or $$H(s) = \frac{1}{(s^2 + 1\cdot 414s + 1)}$$

Typical values of $1/H(s)$ for different n are shown in Table 4.1 and further details are given in Appendix D.

Table 4.1

n	$1/H(s)$
1	$s+1$
2	$s^2 + 1\cdot 414s + 1$
3	$s^3 + 2s^2 + 2s + 1$
4	$s^4 + 2\cdot 613s^3 + 3\cdot 414s^2 + 2\cdot 613s + 1$

A plot of $H(s)$ for various values of n is shown in Fig. 4.1. The amplitude response, because of its initial flatness, is referred to as the 'maximally flat' response over the pass band and is monotonic. In the attenuation band it falls off as ω^{-n} and the roll-off in dB is given by

$$20 \log_{10} H(s) = 20 \log_{10} \frac{1}{\sqrt{1+\omega^{2n}}}$$

$$= 20 \log_{10} \omega^{-n}$$

$$= -20n \log_{10} \omega$$

i.e. the maximum value of dB 'roll-off' is $6n$ dB/octave or $20n$ dB/decade.

Filters are usually designed using 'normalized' values as mentioned earlier, i.e. for $\omega_c = 1$, $R_0 = 1\ \Omega$. The answers obtained are then suitably scaled up to give the exact physical values of the practical filter. For example, if R_0, L, C are the unnormalized filter parameters and R_n, L_n, C_n

are the normalized values, we have that the actual frequency s is related to the normalized frequency s_n by the relation

$$s_n = \frac{s}{\omega_c}$$

where ω_c is taken as the normalizing cut-off frequency.

If only the frequency is normalized but not R_0, then the other impedances must be the same at the appropriate frequency and so we have

$$sL = s_n L_n$$

or

$$L = \frac{s_n L_n}{s} = \frac{L_n}{\omega_c}$$

and

$$\frac{1}{sC} = \frac{1}{s_n C_n}$$

or

$$C = \frac{s_n C_n}{s} = \frac{C_n}{\omega_c}$$

If, furthermore, the level of resistance R of the filter is normalized also, so that

$$R_n = \frac{R}{R_0}$$

or

$$R = R_0 R_n$$

then the actual resistance level R is obtained by multiplying the normalized value by R_0. In the case of an inductance, its impedance is increased by multiplying it by R_0, but for a capacitance, its value of C must be *decreased* by R_0 in order to increase its impedance. Hence, when both frequency and resistance level are normalized, we have the equations

$$R = R_n R_0$$

$$L = \frac{L_n R_0}{\omega_c}$$

$$C = \frac{C_n}{\omega_c R_0}$$

Example 4.1

Design a third-order Butterworth filter with a cut-off frequency $\omega_c = 10^6$ rad/s and a load impedance of 600 Ω. The source impedance is zero.

Solution

The filter elements are designed using normalized values of $\omega_c = 1$ rad/s and a load impedance of 1 Ω.

Since $n = 3$, from Table 4.1 we obtain

$$H(s) = \frac{1}{s^3 + 2s^2 + 2s + 1}$$

For a ladder network, with $n = 3$, there are three reactive components L_1, L_3 and C_2 and the network is as shown in Fig. 4.2.

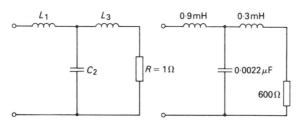

Fig. 4.2

In this case, it can be shown that

$$H(s) = \frac{V_2(s)}{V_1(s)} = \frac{1}{(s^3 L_1 L_3 C_2/R) + s^2 L_1 C_2 + [s(L_1 + L_3)/R] + 1}$$

By equating terms, we obtain

$$\frac{L_1 L_3 C_2}{R} = 1 \quad \text{or} \quad L_1 L_3 C_2 = 1$$

$$L_1 C_2 = 2 \qquad L_1 C_2 = 2$$

$$\frac{L_1 + L_3}{R} = 2 \qquad L_1 + L_3 = 2$$

Hence

$$L_1 = \tfrac{3}{2} \, \text{H}$$
$$L_3 = \tfrac{1}{2} \, \text{H}$$
$$C_2 = \tfrac{4}{3} \, \text{F}$$

To obtain the *denormalized* values R_0', L_1', L_3' and C_2' we have

$$R_0' = R_0 R_n = 600 \times 1 = 600 \, \Omega$$

$$L_1' = \frac{L_1 R_0}{\omega_c} = \frac{3}{2} \times \frac{600}{10^6} = 0.9 \, \text{mH}$$

$$L_3' = \frac{L_3 R_0}{\omega_c} = \frac{1}{2} \times \frac{600}{10^6} = 0.3 \, \text{mH}$$

$$C_2' = \frac{C_2}{\omega_c R_0} = \frac{4}{3 \times 10^6 \times 600} = 0.0022 \, \mu\text{F}$$

4.4   Chebyshev filter[25-27]

The Chebyshev approximation of the ideal low-pass filter response is shown in Fig. 4.3 and given by

$$H_n(s)H_n(-s) = |H_n(s)|^2 = \frac{1}{1 + \varepsilon^2 C_n^2(\omega)}$$

where $\varepsilon < 1$ and $C_n(\omega)$ are the Chebyshev polynomials of order n.

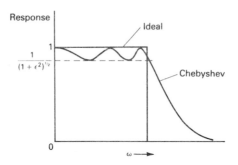

Fig. 4.3

Since the approximation tends to vary in magnitude between equal limits over the pass band, it is often called the 'equi-ripple' approximation.

The Chebyshev polynomials $C_n(\omega)$ are given by

$$C_n(\omega) = \cos(n\cos^{-1}\omega) \quad \text{when} \quad 0 \leqslant \omega \leqslant 1$$

and

$$C_n(\omega) = \cosh(n\cosh^{-1}\omega) \quad \text{when} \quad \omega \geqslant 1$$

Typical values of $C_n(\omega)$ for different n are shown in Table 4.2 and further details are given in Appendix D.

Table 4.2

n	$C_n(\omega)$
1	ω
2	$2\omega^2 - 1$
3	$4\omega^3 - 3\omega$
4	$8\omega^4 - 8\omega^2 + 1$

The 'ripples' vary between 1 and $(1 + \varepsilon^2)^{-1/2}$ giving a *ripple height* of $1 - (1 + \varepsilon^2)^{-1/2}$ over the pass band. Well beyond the pass band, when $\omega > 1$, we have

$$H_n(s) = \frac{1}{\varepsilon C_n(\omega)}$$

or
$$20 \log_{10} H_n(s) = -20 \log_{10} \varepsilon C_n(\omega)$$
$$= -20 \log_{10} \varepsilon - 20 \log_{10} C_n(\omega)$$

For $\omega > 1$, $C_n(\omega) = 2^{n-1}(\omega^n)$

Hence
$$20 \log_{10} H_n(s) = -[20 \log_{10} \varepsilon + 6 \cdot 02(n-1) + 20n \log_{10} \omega]$$

or
$$\text{dB loss} = 20 \log_{10} \varepsilon + 6 \cdot 02(n-1) + 20n \log_{10} \omega$$

At high frequencies, the fall-off is therefore $20n$ dB/decade, the same as for the Butterworth filter. However, this approximation depends upon the two variables ε and n, the former defining the maximum permissible ripple, and the latter the required attenuation.

The poles of the filter are given by
$$1 + \varepsilon^2 C_n^2 \left(\frac{s}{j}\right) = 0$$

or
$$C_n\left(\frac{s}{j}\right) = \pm j\frac{1}{\varepsilon}$$

Now
$$C_n\left(\frac{s}{j}\right) = \cos\left[n \cos^{-1}\left(\frac{s}{j}\right)\right]$$

and it may be assumed that
$$\cos^{-1}\left(\frac{s}{j}\right) = \gamma + j\beta$$

Hence
$$\cos\left[n \cos^{-1}\left(\frac{s}{j}\right)\right] = \cos(n\gamma + nj\beta)$$

or
$$\cos(n\gamma + nj\beta) = \pm j\frac{1}{\varepsilon}$$

Equating real and imaginary parts leads to
$$\cos n\gamma \cosh n\beta = 0$$
$$\sin n\gamma \sinh n\beta = \pm\frac{1}{\varepsilon}$$

Since
$$\cosh n\beta \neq 0$$

we have
$$\cos n\gamma = 0$$

or
$$\gamma = \pm\frac{\pi}{2n}, \pm\frac{3\pi}{2n} \text{ etc.}$$

Hence
$$\sin n\gamma = \pm 1$$

and
$$\sinh n\beta = \frac{1}{\varepsilon}$$

or
$$\beta = \frac{1}{n} \sinh^{-1} \frac{1}{\varepsilon}$$

Since γ and β are thus known, s is obtained from the equation
$$s = j \cos(\gamma + j\beta)$$

or
$$s = \sin \gamma \sinh \beta + j \cos \gamma \cosh \beta$$

As an example let $n = 2$ and $\varepsilon = 0\cdot5$

Hence
$$\gamma = \pm \frac{\pi}{4}$$

$$\beta = \tfrac{1}{2} \sinh^{-1} \frac{1}{0\cdot5} = 0\cdot72$$

and
$$s = \sin \frac{\pi}{4} \sinh 0\cdot72 \pm j \cos \frac{\pi}{4} \cosh 0\cdot72$$

or
$$s_1 = 0\cdot554 + j0\cdot9$$
$$s_2 = 0\cdot554 - j0\cdot9$$

and
$$H(s) = \frac{1}{(s + s_1)(s + s_2)}$$

$$= \frac{1}{(s + 0\cdot554 + j0\cdot9)(s + 0\cdot554 - j0\cdot9)}$$

or
$$H(s) = \frac{1}{s^2 + 1\cdot108s + 1\cdot117}$$

Example 4.2

Design a Chebyshev low-pass filter with a cut-off frequency of 10^4 rad/s and a design impedance of $600\ \Omega$. The ripple in the pass band must not exceed $0\cdot5$ dB and the response after cut-off must be -60 dB/decade.

Solution

The response after cut-off is $-20n$ dB/decade and so $n = 3$ i.e. it must be a third-order filter. The ripple amplitude in the pass band is given by

$$20 \log (1 + \varepsilon^2)^{1/2} = 0\cdot5$$

or $$(1 + \varepsilon^2) = 1 \cdot 22$$

and $$\varepsilon = 0 \cdot 349$$

Assuming normalised values of $\omega_c = 1$, $R_0 = 1\,\Omega$, β is obtained from the equation

$$\beta = (1/n)\sinh^{-1}(1/\varepsilon)$$
$$= (1/3)\sinh^{-1}(1/0 \cdot 349)$$
$$= (1/3)\sinh^{-1}(2 \cdot 865)$$

or $$\beta = (1/3) \times 1 \cdot 78 = 0 \cdot 59$$

Also $$\sin n\gamma = \pm 1$$

or $$\gamma = \pm \frac{\pi}{2n}, \ \pm \frac{3\pi}{2n}$$

Hence $$\gamma = +\frac{\pi}{6}, \ -\frac{\pi}{6}, \ +\frac{\pi}{2}$$

The poles are s_1, s_2, s_3 where

$$s_1 = j\cos(\gamma + j\beta)$$
$$= \sin\gamma \sinh\beta + j\cos\gamma \cosh\beta$$
$$= \sin(\pi/6)\sinh 0 \cdot 59 + j\cos(\pi/6)\cosh 0 \cdot 59$$
$$= 0 \cdot 5 \times 0 \cdot 6248 + j\, 0 \cdot 866 \times 1 \cdot 1792$$

or $$s_1 = 0 \cdot 31 + j\, 1 \cdot 02$$
$$s_2 = 0 \cdot 31 - j\, 1 \cdot 02 \text{ (conjugate pole)}$$
$$s_3 = \sin(\pi/2)\sinh 0 \cdot 59 = 1 \times 0 \cdot 6248$$

or $$s_3 = 0 \cdot 62$$

and $$H(s) = \frac{1}{(s + 0 \cdot 31 + j1 \cdot 02)(s + 0 \cdot 31 - j1 \cdot 02)(s + 0 \cdot 62)}$$

or $$H(s) = \frac{1}{1 \cdot 43s^3 + 1 \cdot 77s^2 + 2 \cdot 17s + 1}$$

By equating coefficients as in Example 4.1 we obtain

$$\frac{L_1 L_3 C_2}{R} = 1 \cdot 43 \qquad L_3 = \frac{1 \cdot 43}{1 \cdot 77} = 0 \cdot 80\ \text{H}$$

$$L_1 C_2 = 1 \cdot 77 \qquad L_1 = 2 \cdot 17 - 0 \cdot 8 = 1 \cdot 37\ \text{H}$$

$$L_1 + L_3 = 2 \cdot 17 \qquad C_2 = \frac{1 \cdot 77}{1 \cdot 37} = 1 \cdot 29\ \text{F}$$

Denormalising to $\omega = 10^4$ rad/s and $R = 600\,\Omega$ yields

$$R_1 = R_0 R_n = 600 \times 1 = 600 \ \Omega$$

$$L_1' = \frac{L_1 R_0}{\omega_c} = \frac{1 \cdot 37 \times 600}{10^4} = 0 \cdot 082 \ \text{H}$$

$$L_3' = \frac{L_3 R_0}{\omega_c} = \frac{0 \cdot 8 \times 600}{10^4} = 0 \cdot 048 \ \text{H}$$

$$C_2' = \frac{C_2}{\omega_c R_0} = \frac{1 \cdot 29}{10^4 \times 600} = 0 \cdot 22 \ \mu\text{F}$$

The network is shown in Fig. 4.4.

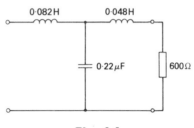

Fig. 4.4

4.5   Elliptic function filters[5-6, 28-29]

These filters are characterised by having both poles and zeros. The zeros occur in both the pass band and stop band and they give the steepest rate of cut off possible (between the pass and stop bands), for a given number of sections. The positions of the zeros are related to the elliptic functions of classical field theory, hence the name *elliptic function* filters. The filters are also called *Cauer* filters because of the original work by Cauer on the subject.

However, the design leads to equiripples in both the pass band and the stop band and so it is necessary to specify both the pass band ripple and the minimum stop band attenuation required. The pass band ripples are similar to those of the Chebyshev filter, while the stop band ripples are also equal in amplitude.

The transfer function of the low-pass filter is of the form

$$|H_n(s)|^2 = \frac{1}{1 + \varepsilon^2 R_n^2(\omega)}$$

where $0 < \varepsilon < 1$ and $R_n(\omega)$ is the Chebyshev rational function of order n.

If A_p and A_s are the attenuation factors in the pass and stop bands respectively, let ω_p and ω_s be the corresponding critical frequencies. The filter is normalised at $\omega_c = 1$, with the maximum pass band ripple attenuation at $\omega_p = \omega_c$ and maximum stop band attenuation at ω_s as shown in Fig. 4.5. This leads to the conditions

$$A_1 = \frac{1}{1 + \varepsilon^2 R_{max}^2}$$

where R_{max} is the maximum value of $|R_n(\omega)|$ for $|\omega| \leqslant \omega_p$ and

$$A_2 = \frac{1}{1 + \varepsilon^2 R_{min}^2}$$

where R_{min} is the minimum value of $|R_n(\omega)|$ for $|\omega| \geqslant \omega_s$. Furthermore, as the poles of $R_n(\omega)$ are symmetric about $\omega_c = 1$ we have

$$R_{min} = 1/R_{max}$$

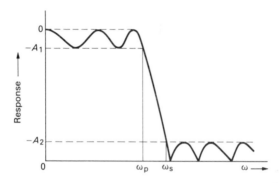

Fig. 4.5

Example 4.3

Design a low-pass elliptic function filter with less than 0·5 dB attenuation in the pass band at 3 kHz and with greater than 40 dB attenuation in the stop band at 5 kHz. The filter is designed to work into a load resistance of 600 Ω.

Solution
The stop band to pass band frequency ratio is given by

$$\frac{\omega_s}{\omega_p} = \frac{5 \times 10^3}{3 \times 10^3} = 1\cdot67$$

and if $\omega_p = 1$ by normalisation, we obtain $\omega_s = 1\cdot67$.

From standard tables given in Appendix D (Table D.4) we observe that for a maximum value of $\omega_s = 1\cdot67$ and with less than 0·5 dB ripple in the pass band, we must choose a value of $A_1 = 0\cdot1$ dB and a fifth-order filter. In this case, the nearest values of $\omega_s = 1\cdot54$ and $A_2 = 45$ dB meet our filter requirements. The normalised filter components are shown in Fig. 4.6(a).

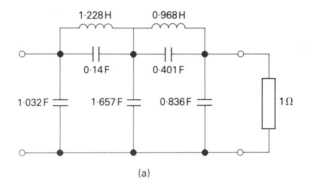

(a)

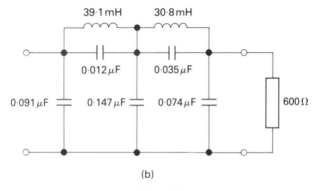

(b)

Fig. 4.6

To obtain the denormalised component values R, L and C we use the expressions:

$$R = R_n R_0$$
$$L = L_n R_0 / \omega_c$$
$$C = C_n / \omega_c R_0$$

where R_n, L_n and C_n are the normalised component values, the load resistance $R_0 = 600\ \Omega$ and the cut-off frequency $\omega_c = \omega_p$. The final filter design is shown in Fig. 4.6(b).

4.6   Frequency transformation

The previous design procedures have been applied essentially to low-pass filters. However, the high-pass filter can be designed simply by replacing inductors with capacitors, and capacitors with inductors, having the same reactance at the normalized frequency. The response characteristic is identical to that of the low-pass case and the frequency scale is inverted about the normalized frequency.

Band-pass filters are designed from low-pass filters by choosing the normalized point equal to the geometric mean of the bandwidth of the filter. Capacitors are then placed in series with inductors and with inductors in parallel with capacitors, such that the latter produce branch resonance at the centre frequency.

Band-stop filters may likewise be designed from the high-pass filter. The latter is scaled to a frequency which gives the rejection bandwidth required for the band-stop filter. Inductors and capacitors are then added to each branch in the same way as for the band-pass filter, with each branch resonating at the desired centre frequency which is the point of maximum attenuation.

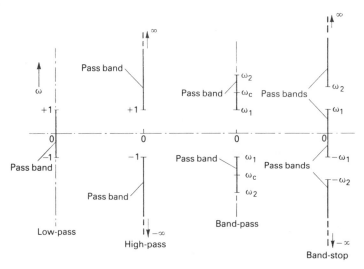

Fig. 4.7

(a) High-pass filter

If s is any frequency variable and s_n is the normalized frequency for a *low-pass* filter with cut-off ω_c then

$$s_n = \frac{s}{\omega_c}$$

where $s = j\omega$.

For a high-pass filter, the frequency is inverted about the cut-off value such that

$$s_n = \frac{\omega_c}{s}$$

or
$$s = \frac{\omega_c}{s_n}$$

Hence, over the pass-band, ω_n for the low-pass filter lies between $-1 \leqslant \omega_n \leqslant 1$, and so ω_n for the high-pass filter varies between ∞ and 1 or ∞ and -1.

To obtain the component values, let L_n and C_n be the component values for the low-pass filter and L_h, C_h those for the high-pass filter. Remembering that the components are interchanged with the same reactance, we have

$$s_n L_n = \frac{\omega_c L_n}{s} = \frac{1}{sC_h}$$

and
$$\frac{1}{s_n C_n} = \frac{s}{\omega_c C_n} = sL_h$$

Hence
$$L_h = \frac{1}{\omega_c C_n}$$

$$C_h = \frac{1}{\omega_c L_n}$$

The transformation is shown in Fig. 4.7.

(b) Band-pass filter

The transformation from low-pass to band-pass is made by using the substitution

$$s_n = \frac{\omega_c}{\omega_2 - \omega_1} \left[\frac{s}{\omega_c} + \frac{\omega_c}{s} \right]$$

where $\omega_1 < \omega_2$ and ω_1, ω_2 are the two cut-off frequencies of the band-pass filter. Moreover, ω_c is the geometric mean frequency and is given by

$$\omega_c = \sqrt{\omega_1 \omega_2}$$

Hence
$$s_n = \frac{(s^2 + \omega_1 \omega_2)}{s(\omega_2 - \omega_1)}$$

If the low-pass components are L_n and C_n, L_n transforms into a series L_s and C_s while C_n transforms into a parallel L_p and C_p. Their values are given by the equations

$$s_n L_n = \frac{\omega_c L_n}{\omega_2 - \omega_1} \left[\frac{s}{\omega_c} + \frac{\omega_c}{s} \right] = sL_s + \frac{1}{sC_s}$$

i.e. a series L_s and C_s.

Also
$$\frac{1}{s_n C_n} = \frac{\dfrac{1}{C_n}\left[\dfrac{\omega_2 - \omega_1}{\omega_c}\right]}{\left(\dfrac{s}{\omega_c} + \dfrac{\omega_c}{s}\right)}$$

$$= \frac{\dfrac{(\omega_2 - \omega_1)^2}{\omega_c^2 C_n^2}}{\dfrac{s(\omega_2 - \omega_1)}{\omega_c C_n} + \dfrac{(\omega_2 - \omega_1)}{s C_n}}$$

which is equivalent to

$$\frac{sL_p \times \dfrac{1}{sC_p}}{sL_p + \dfrac{1}{sC_p}}$$

i.e. a parallel L_p and C_p.

Hence we obtain by equating terms

$$L_s = \frac{L_n}{(\omega_2 - \omega_1)} \qquad C_s = \frac{\omega_2 - \omega_1}{\omega_c^2 L_n}$$

$$L_p = \frac{(\omega_2 - \omega_1)}{\omega_c^2 C_n} \qquad C_p = \frac{C_n}{(\omega_2 - \omega_1)}$$

The transformation is shown in Fig. 4.7.

(c) Band-stop filter

The transformation is obtained by modifying the expression for s_n as used in the band-pass case to give

$$s_n = \frac{\omega_2 - \omega_1}{\omega_c\left(\dfrac{s}{\omega_c} + \dfrac{\omega_c}{s}\right)}$$

or

$$s_n = \frac{s(\omega_2 - \omega_1)}{(s^2 + \omega_1 \omega_2)}$$

In this case, the series L_n transforms into a parallel L_p, C_p and the shunt C_n transforms into a series L_s, C_s. They are given by the equations

$$s_n L_n = \frac{L_n(\omega_2 - \omega_1)}{\omega_c\left(\dfrac{s}{\omega_c} + \dfrac{\omega_c}{s}\right)} = \frac{\dfrac{L_n^2}{\omega_c^2}(\omega_2 - \omega_1)^2}{\dfrac{sL_n(\omega_2 - \omega_1)}{\omega_c^2} + \dfrac{1}{s}L_n(\omega_2 - \omega_1)}$$

74   *Networks*

which is equivalent to

$$\frac{sL_p \times \dfrac{1}{sC_p}}{sL_p + \dfrac{1}{sC_p}}$$

i.e. a parallel L_p and C_p.
 Also

$$\frac{1}{s_n C_n} = \frac{1}{C_n}\left[\frac{\omega_c}{\omega_2 - \omega_1}\right]\left(\frac{s}{\omega_c} + \frac{\omega_c}{s}\right) = \frac{s}{(\omega_2 - \omega_1)C_n} + \frac{1}{s}\frac{\omega_c^2}{(\omega_2 - \omega_1)C_n}$$

which is equivalent to

$$sL_s + \frac{1}{sC_s}$$

i.e. a series L_s and C_s.
 Hence we obtain by equating terms

$$L_p = \frac{L_n(\omega_2 - \omega_1)}{\omega_c^2} \qquad C_p = \frac{1}{(\omega_2 - \omega_1)L_n}$$

$$L_s = \frac{1}{(\omega_2 - \omega_1)C_n} \qquad C_s = \frac{(\omega_2 - \omega_1)C_n}{\omega_c^2}$$

The transformation is shown in Fig. 4.7.

Example 4.4
Design a band-pass filter from the normalized low-pass structure shown in
Fig. 4.8(a). The centre frequency is 4×10^4 rad/s. Determine the component values
for a load impedance of 600 Ω.

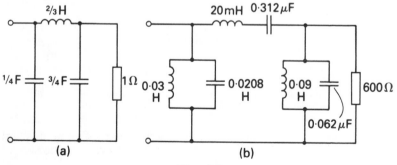

Fig. 4.8

Solution
Using impedance denormalization of the low-pass filter only yields, for a load
impedance of 600 Ω,

$$R_0' = R_0 R_n = 600 \times 1 = 600\,\Omega$$

$$L_n' = L_n R_0 = \tfrac{2}{3} \times 600 = 400\,\text{H}$$

$$C_{n_1}' = \frac{C_{n_1}}{R_0} = \frac{1}{4 \times 600} = \frac{1250}{3}\,\mu\text{F}$$

$$C_{n_2}' = \frac{C_{n_2}}{R_0} = \frac{3}{4 \times 600} = 1250\,\mu\text{F}$$

For a band-pass transformation, the inductance becomes a series L_s and C_s, given by (see section 4.6(b))

$$L_s = \frac{L_n'}{\omega_2 - \omega_1} = \frac{400}{2 \times 10^4} - 20\,\text{mH}$$

$$C_s = \frac{\omega_2 - \omega_1}{\omega_c^2 L_n'} = \frac{2 \times 10^4}{(4 \times 10^4)^2 \times 400} = 0\cdot312\,\mu\text{F}$$

The capacitances C_{n_1}' and C_{n_2}' transform into parallel L_p and C_p given by

$$L_{p1} = \frac{\omega_2 - \omega_1}{\omega_c^2 C_{n_1}'} = \frac{2 \times 10^4 \times 3 \times 10^6}{(4 \times 10^4)^2 \times 1250} = 0\cdot03\,\text{H}$$

$$C_{p1} = \frac{C_{n_1}'}{\omega_2 - \omega_1} = \frac{1250 \times 10^{-6}}{3 \times 2 \times 10^4} = 0\cdot0208\,\mu\text{F}$$

$$L_{p2} = \frac{\omega_2 - \omega_1}{\omega_c^2 C_{n_2}'} = \frac{2 \times 10^4 \times 10^6}{(4 \times 10^4)^2 \times 1250} = 0\cdot09\,\text{H}$$

$$C_{p2} = \frac{C_{n_2}'}{\omega_2 - \omega_1} = \frac{1250 \times 10^{-6}}{2 \times 10^4} = 0\cdot06\,\mu\text{F}$$

The filter is shown in Fig. 4.8(b).

5
Active filters

In order to achieve the usual transfer functions attainable with passive LC filters, the design of RC filters requires the use of some active device to achieve similar results. Filters constructed with one or more transistors as the active device are known as *active filters*[30-33]. Such filters are especially suitable for operation at the lower frequencies up to about 500 kHz or more. They are finding greater use in many applications because one advantage in the use of RC filters is the elimination of bulky expensive inductances.

In recent years, the considerable advance in thick and thin film technology lends itself to the relative ease and low cost with which such devices can be constructed. Moreover, some of the sensitivity problems associated with such circuits are being gradually overcome and there is an increasing confidence in the use of active filters.

Three important devices used in the design of RC active filters are the negative-impedance converter (NIC), the gyrator, and the operational amplifier (op amp). The NIC was largely used in the early days of active filter design but has now largely given place to the use of op-amps only or gyrators constructed with op-amps.

5.1 Negative-impedance converter (NIC)

The ideal negative-impedance converter shown in Fig. 5.1(a) is a two-port device whose input impedance Z_i is equal to the negative of the load

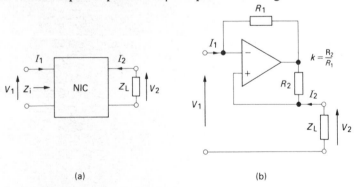

(a)   (b)

Fig. 5.1

impedance Z_L i.e. $Z_i = -Z_L$. There are two types of NICs, the voltage inversion NIC (VNIC) or the current inversion NIC (CNIC). An example of a VNIC is shown in Fig. 5.1(b).

Using g-parameters, we obtain the basic equations

$$I_1 = g_{11}V_1 + g_{12}I_2$$
$$V_2 = g_{21}V_1 + g_{22}I_2$$

with

$$Z_L = V_2/-I_2$$
$$Y_i = I_1/V_1$$

or

$$Y_i = g_{11} - \frac{g_{12} \cdot g_{21}}{g_{22} + Z_L}$$

If $g_{11} = g_{22} = 0$ and $g_{12} \cdot g_{21} = 1$, then we obtain

$$Y_i = -1/Z_L$$

or

$$Z_i = -Z_L$$

The NIC is a two-port device and by means of the A, B, C, D parameters it can also be represented by a transmission matrix of the form

$$\begin{bmatrix} V_1 \\ I_1 \end{bmatrix} = \begin{bmatrix} 1 & 0 \\ 0 & -k \end{bmatrix} \begin{bmatrix} V_2 \\ -I_2 \end{bmatrix}$$

for a VNIC or of the form

$$\begin{bmatrix} V_1 \\ I_1 \end{bmatrix} = \begin{bmatrix} -k & 0 \\ 0 & 1 \end{bmatrix} \begin{bmatrix} V_2 \\ -I_2 \end{bmatrix}$$

for a CNIC, where k is a positive constant. The generalised input impedance is then given by $Z_i = -Z_L/k$ and the equivalent circuits for the VNIC and CNIC respectively are shown in Fig. 5.2. A typical VNIC is the circuit of Linvill[30].

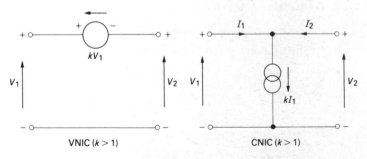

VNIC ($k > 1$)   CNIC ($k > 1$)

Fig. 5.2

Comment
The present disuse of the NIC is due mainly to its high sensitivity and relative inconvenience for monolithic fabrication.

5.2 The gyrator[34-35]

The ideal gyrator circuit shown in Fig. 5.3(a) is a non-reciprocal two-port device whose input impedance Z_i is the reciprocal of the load impedance Z_L i.e. $Z_i = R^2/Z_L$ where R is the gyration resistance. An ideal gyrator is more easily realised using op-amps and is shown in Fig. 5.3(b).

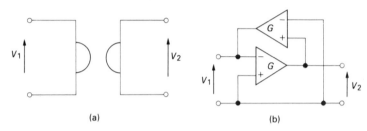

(a)   (b)

Fig. 5.3

Using y-parameters we obtain the basic equations

$$I_1 = y_{11}V_1 + y_{12}V_2$$
$$I_2 = y_{21}V_1 + y_{22}V_2$$

with
$$Y_L = I_2/V_2$$

and
$$Y_{in} = I_1/V_1$$

or
$$Y_{in} = y_{11} - \frac{y_{12}\,y_{21}}{y_{22} + Y_L}$$

where Y_L is the load admittance.

If
$$y_{11} = y_{22} = 0 \quad \text{and} \quad y_{12}\,y_{21} = -G^2$$

where $G = 1/R$ is the gyration conductance, then

$$Y_i = G^2/Y_L$$

or
$$Z_i = R^2/Z_L$$

Furthermore, if $y_{12} = G$ and $y_{21} = -G$ then

$$I_1 = GV_2$$
$$I_2 = -GV_1$$

or
$$\begin{bmatrix} I_1 \\ I_2 \end{bmatrix} = \begin{bmatrix} 0 & G \\ -G & 0 \end{bmatrix} \begin{bmatrix} V_1 \\ V_2 \end{bmatrix}$$

and
$$[I] = [Y][V]$$

where
$$[Y] = \begin{bmatrix} 0 & G \\ -G & 0 \end{bmatrix}$$

Since I_1 is proportional to V_2 while I_2 is proportional to $-V_1$, the device is non-reciprocal. Moreover, the admittance matrix Y can be written as the sum of two admittance matrices in parallel viz.

$$\begin{bmatrix} 0 & G \\ -G & 0 \end{bmatrix} = \begin{bmatrix} 0 & 0 \\ -G & 0 \end{bmatrix} + \begin{bmatrix} 0 & G \\ 0 & 0 \end{bmatrix}$$

or
$$[Y] = [Y_1] + [Y_2]$$

where $[Y_1]$ and $[Y_2]$ are each a voltage-controlled current source (VCCS) such as an op-amp. Thus, the gyrator can be constructed by using an op-amp in parallel with another as shown in Fig. 5.3(b).

The gyrator was first proposed by Telegen[34] and because of its impedance inverting property it behaves as an inductance when terminated by a capacitance. This useful property can be used to replace physical inductances in filters, by means of gyrators. An example of a 'floating' inductor realisation is shown in Fig. 5.4(a) and a 'grounded' inductor realisation, in Fig. 5.4(b).

Various types of gyrator circuits have been devised and a circuit due to Antiniou[36] uses a cascade arrangement which is illustrated in Fig. 5.5.

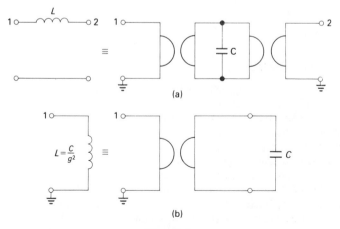

(a)

(b)

Fig. 5.4

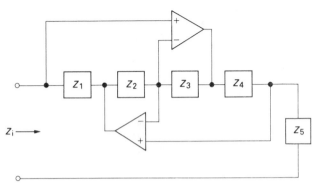

Fig. 5.5

It can be shown that the input impedance Z_i of this circuit is given by

$$Z_i = Z_1 Z_3 Z_5 / Z_2 Z_4$$

and if $Z_1 = Z_2$ we obtain

$$Z_i = Z_3 Z_5 / Z_4$$

Furthermore, if the impedances Z_3 and Z_5 are resistive such that $Z_3 = R_3$ and $Z_5 = R_5$, while Z_4 is due to a capacitance C_4 with $Z_4 = 1/sC_4$, we obtain

$$Z_i = sR_3 R_5 C_4$$

or $$Z_i = sL_{eq}$$

where $L_{eq} = R_3 R_5 C_4$ is the equivalent inductance which appears at the input. Gyrators of this type can have Q-values of about 1000 and inductance values of 0.1 H to 1 H.

5.3   Operational amplifiers[37]

An ideal operational amplifier or op amp as it is often called, has an infinite voltage gain, an infinite input impedance, an infinite bandwidth and a zero output impedance. A non-ideal or practical op amp, however, has a high voltage gain around 100 dB, a high input impedance of about 0.5 MΩ, a low output impedance around $100\,\Omega$ and a finite bandwidth.

The op amp can be used for performing various mathematical operations such as summing, differentiating, integrating, inverting etc. and is a very versatile 'building block' in the construction of such circuits as active filters, comparators or logarithmic amplifiers. Its present popularity is largely due to its low cost as an integrated circuit (IC), a form in which it is now widely used.

(a) Ideal operation

The circuit symbol of an op amp is shown in Fig. 5.6(a). It is depicted as a three-terminal device (relative to ground) with the two input terminals (1) and (2) designated with minus $(-)$ and plus $(+)$ signs respectively. Terminal (1) is the *inverting* terminal because a positive voltage applied to this terminal produces a negative output voltage at terminal (3), and terminal (2) is the non-inverting terminal because a positive voltage applied to this terminal produces a positive output voltage at terminal (3). An op amp integrated circuit view is shown in Fig. 5.6(b).

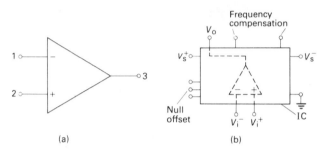

(a)   (b)

Fig. 5.6

Inverting amplifier
For the inverting amplifier shown in Fig. 5.7(a), R_i is the input series resistor and negative feedback is applied from the output terminal (3) to the input terminal (1) via the feedback resistor R_f.

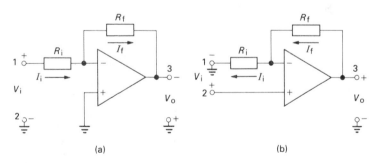

(a)   (b)

Fig. 5.7

If V_i is the input voltage and V_o is the output voltage, the input current I_i and feedback current I_f are given by

$$I_i = V_i/R_i$$
$$I_f = -V_o/R_f$$

since the input impedance of the amplifier is infinite and no current can flow into it. The terminal with the minus sign $(-)$ is therefore effectively at ground potential or at 'virtual earth'. Thus

$$I_i = I_f$$

or

$$V_i/R_i = -V_o/R_f$$

with

$$V_o/V_i = -R_f/R_i$$

or

$$A = -R_f/R_i$$

and so the gain of the amplifier is determined purely by the ratio of the two external resistances R_f and R_i.

Non-inverting amplifier
For the non-inverting amplifier shown in Fig. 5.7(b) we similarly have

$$I_f = I_i$$

with

$$V_i = I_i R_i$$

and

$$V_o = I_f R_f + I_i R_i$$

Hence

$$V_o/V_i = \frac{I_f R_f + I_i R_i}{I_i R_i} = \frac{(R_f + R_i)}{R_i}$$

or

$$A = 1 + R_f/R_i$$

and so the gain of the amplifier again depends also on the ratio of the two external resistances R_f and R_i.

(b)   Non-ideal operation
The essential difference between an ideal op amp and a non-ideal op amp is in the realisation of amplifier gain. For practical reasons, the latter must have a finite open-loop gain which at d.c. is denoted by A_o. Furthermore, at higher frequencies, to avoid instability due to oscillations (if the phase shift exceeds 180°), the closed-loop gain A_c must fall to unity at some high frequency f_h. Hence, a typical gain-frequency characteristic of a practical op amp is shown in Fig. 5.8. The 3 dB point is defined at some low frequency value f_l and so the (unity gain × bandwidth) product occurs at the frequency value of f_h. The final roll-off is at a rate of 6 dB/octave.

Inverting amplifier
From feedback theory, the closed-loop gain A_c is given by

$$A_c = \frac{A_o(\beta - 1)}{1 + A_o \beta}$$

where the feedback factor $\beta = R_i/(R_i + R_f)$.

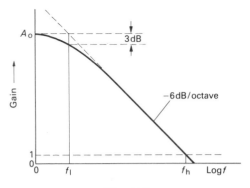

Fig. 5.8

Hence

$$(\beta - 1) = -R_f/(R_i + R_f)$$

and

$$A_c = \frac{-A_o R_f}{(R_i + R_f)} \Bigg/ \left[1 + \frac{A_o R_i}{(R_i + R_f)} \right]$$

or

$$A_c = \frac{-(R_f/R_i)}{\left[1 + \dfrac{1}{A_o} + \dfrac{R_f}{A_o R_i} \right]}$$

Non-inverting amplifier
From feedback theory, the closed-loop gain A_c is given by

$$A_c = \frac{A_o}{(1 + A_o \beta)}$$

where the feedback factor $\beta = R_i/(R_i + R_f)$.
Hence

$$A_c = \frac{A_o}{1 + A_o [R_i/(R_i + R_f)]}$$

or

$$A_c = \frac{(1 + R_f/R_i)}{1 + \dfrac{1}{A_o} [1 + R_f/R_i]}$$

Op amp integrator
An op amp integrator can be obtained from the inverting amplifier by
replacing the feedback resistor R_f with a capacitor C and with $R_i = R$. Such
a circuit is known as a Miller integrator and is shown in Fig. 5.9.

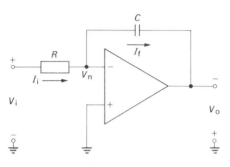

Fig. 5.9

For a non-ideal amplifier with finite gain A_c and a node voltage V_n we have

$$\frac{(V_i - V_n)}{R} + C \frac{d(V_o - V_n)}{dt} = 0$$

or

$$\int d(V_o - V_n) = -\frac{1}{RC} \int (V_i - V_n)\, dt$$

with

$$(V_o - V_n) = -\frac{1}{RC} \frac{(V_i - V_n)}{p} = -\frac{(V_i - V_n)}{pRC}$$

where $(1/p)$ signifies integration.

Since $A_c = -V_o/V_n$, substituting for V_n yields

$$V_o + V_o/A_c = \frac{-(V_i + V_o/A_c)}{pRC}$$

or

$$V_o \left[1 + \frac{1}{A_c}\left(1 + \frac{1}{pRC}\right) \right] = -\frac{V_i}{p\,RC}$$

and

$$\frac{V_o}{V_i} = \frac{-1}{pRC} \left[\frac{1}{1 + \dfrac{1}{A_c}\left(1 + \dfrac{1}{pRC}\right)} \right]$$

Comment

Since A_c is infinite for an *ideal* op amp, we obtain from the last expression above

$$V_o/V_i = -1/pRC$$

for an integrator employing an ideal op amp.

(c) Practical considerations

A typical op amp is a dual-input differential amplifier which is followed by one or more direct coupled stages. Op amps often employ two direct-coupled differential amplifiers in cascade which are followed by an output stage for additional gain. The direct interstage coupling is ideally suited for bipolar integrated circuit technology. More recently, CMOS techniques have been employed to produce op amps with low-power consumption.

Typical op amps such as the μA 741 have open-loop gains of about 200 000 at d.c. decreasing monotonically to unity at about 1 MHz, thus yielding a (unity gain × bandwidth) product of 1 MHz. Most op amps like the μA 741 are internally compensated for stability reasons but some like the 709 type require an external compensating network. Op amps usually have two power supply terminals and some provide an input terminal for the nulling of output d.c. offsets. The terminology usually associated with op amps is detailed in Appendix E.

5.4 Active filter design

Any active filter design may be represented by a general transfer function $H(s)$ which is the product of lower order transfer functions and is expressed by

$$H(s) = H_1(s)H_2(s)H_3(s) \ldots H_n(s)$$

where $H_1(s)$, $H_2(s)$ etc. are transfer functions of lower order than $H(s)$.

In particular, for a first-order transfer function we have

$$H_1(s) = \frac{a_1 s + a_2}{b_1 s + b_2}$$

and for a second-order transfer function we have

$$H_2(s) = \frac{a_1 s^2 + a_2 s + a_3}{b_1 s^2 + b_2 s + b_3}$$

where a_1, a_2 etc. and b_1, b_2 etc. are arbitrary constants. Thus, any general transfer function of order $n > 2$ can be expressed in terms of products of first-order and second-order transfer functions.

In practice, second-order active filters are commonly used and are characterised in terms of a quality factor Q and a pole frequency ω_p which are given respectively by

$$Q \triangleq \sqrt{b_1 b_3}/b_2$$

$$\omega_p \triangleq \sqrt{b_3/b_1}$$

where the Q-factor approximately corresponds to the usual definition for resonant circuits. For most applications, the second-order filter is satis-factory and to obtain any filter of higher order, various orders of filters may be cascaded.

Two design schemes used for constructing active filters are known as the direct approach scheme and the cascade approach scheme. In the former case, the desired filter response is obtained using a single block of circuitry as with conventional L, C, R filters, together with modern approximation theory and realisable functions such as those of Butterworth, Chebyshev and elliptic functions.

An example of the direct approach is the second-order Sallen and Key circuit shown in Fig. 5.10 for a typical low-pass filter which employs an op amp with positive feedback and a non-inverting gain of K.

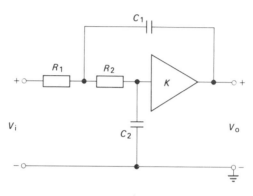

Fig. 5.10

In the cascade approach as mentioned earlier, the filter response is realised by cascading various blocks of first- and second-order filters. This is more useful from the practical design point of view as each block can be separately constructed and adjusted, but it yields more sensitive circuits than those obtained by the direct approach.

Example 5.1

In the low-pass filter circuit shown in Fig. 5.11, obtain an expression for the transfer function of the active filter assuming an ideal operational amplifier with a non-inverting gain K. Furthermore, if $R_1 = R_2 = R$ and $C_1 = C_2 = C$, determine the quality factor and pole frequency of the circuit.

Solution

The filter circuit employs positive feedback from output to input and the gain of the amplifier is adjusted by means of the potentiometer ratio R_4/R_3 with $K = 1 + R_4/R_3$. If the input and output voltages are V_i and V_o respectively, let the node voltage at n be denoted by V_n.

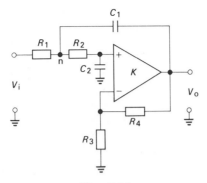

Fig. 5.11

For currents into node n we must have

$$g_i V_i + \left(\frac{V_o}{K}\right)g_2 + V_o sC_1 - (g_1 + g_2 + sC_1)V_n = 0 \tag{1}$$

where $g_1 = 1/R_1$, $g_2 = 1/R_2$ and $s = j\omega$.

For an ideal op amp, the input impedance is infinite and no current flows into the op amp input. Hence, we obtain

$$(V_n - V_o/K)g_2 = \left(\frac{V_o}{K}\right)sC_2$$

or

$$V_n = \frac{V_o(g_2 + sC_2)}{Kg_2} \tag{2}$$

Substituting this value of V_n into equation (1) above and rearranging terms now yields

$$KV_i g_1 g_2 = V_o[g_1 g_2 + g_1 sC_2 + g_2 sC_2 + g_2 sC_1 + s^2 C_1 C_2 - Kg_2 sC_1]$$

The transfer function of the network is given by

$$H(s) = \frac{V_o}{V_i} = \frac{Kg_1 g_2}{[g_1 g_2 + s\{g_1 C_2 + g_2 C_2 + (1-K)g_2 C_1\} + s^2 C_1 C_2]}$$

or

$$H(s) = \frac{K}{[s^2 R_1 R_2 C_1 C_2 + s\{(R_1 + R_2)C_2 + R_1 C_1(1-K)\} + 1]}$$

Arbitrarily, if $R_1 = R_2 = R$ and $C_1 = C_2 = C$, we obtain

$$H(s) = \frac{K}{[s^2 R^2 C^2 + sRC(3-K) + 1]}$$

Hence, the quality factor Q and the pole frequency ω_p are given by

$$Q = \frac{RC}{RC(3-K)} = \frac{1}{(3-K)}$$

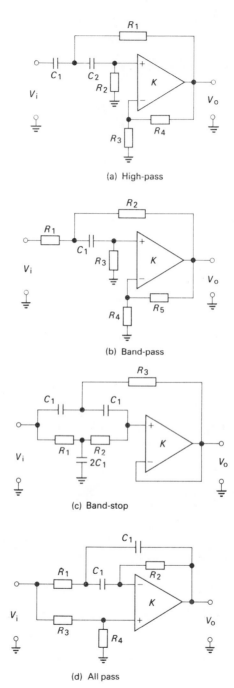

(a) High-pass

(b) Band-pass

(c) Band-stop

(d) All pass

Fig. 5.12

and
$$\omega_p = \frac{1}{RC}$$

Comment

For convenience, if $R = 1\,\Omega$ and $C = 1\,F$, we obtain $\omega_p = 1$. Furthermore, if $Q = 1/\sqrt{2}$ then $K = 3 - \sqrt{2} = 1\cdot586$. The transfer function can now be written in the form

$$H(s) = \frac{1\cdot586}{s^2 + s\sqrt{2} + 1}$$

which represents a second-order Butterworth low-pass filter with a normalised cut-off frequency $\omega_c = \omega_p = 1$.

5.5 Filter realisations

Typical examples of some filter realisations are shown in Fig. 5.12 and their transfer functions are given in Table 5.1. These circuits employ a single operational amplifier together with RC networks. Butterworth or Chebyshev designs may be employed for the first three cases only, depending upon the choice of component values used.

Another realisation is the biquad circuit[38, 39] which uses more components, but achieves a much higher Q-value and a very low sensitivity to component variations.

Table 5.1

High-pass

$$H(s) = \frac{Ks^2/R_1 R_2 C_1 C_2}{s^2 + s\left\{\dfrac{R_1 C_1 + R_1 C_2 + R_2 C_2(1 - K)}{R_1 R_2 C_1 C_2}\right\} + \dfrac{1}{R_1 R_2 C_1 C_2}}$$

$$K = 1 + (R_4/R_3)$$

Band-pass

$$H(s) = \frac{K/R_1 C_1}{s^2 + s\left\{\dfrac{R_2 R_3 + 2R_1 R_2 + R_1 R_3(1 - K)}{R_1 R_2 R_3 C_1}\right\} + \dfrac{(R_1 + R_2)}{R_1 R_2 R_3 C_1^2}}$$

$$K = 1 + (R_5/R_4)$$

Band-stop

$$H(s) = \frac{s^2 + 1/R_1 R_2 C_1^2}{s^2 + s\{2/R_2 C_1\} + 1/R_1 R_2 C_1^2}$$

$$K = 1$$

All pass

$$H(s) = \frac{K[s^2 - s(2/R_2 C_1) + 1/R_1 R_2 C_1^2]}{s^2 + s(2/R_2 C_1) + 1/R_1 R_2 C_1^2}$$

$$K = R_4/(R_3 + R_4)$$

5.6   Higher-order filters

As pointed out earlier, a filter of higher order can be obtained by cascading a number of sections of lower order. To design these sections, the desired transfer function of the filter is written as the product of second-order transfer functions and possibly one of first order, in the case of an odd order filter. The second order stages are then cascaded so that the quadratic factors are multiplied together to give the desired overall response.

However, in this configuration, rather high voltages may occur in the various sections, particularly those with high Q poles. To avoid this, a high Q section is cascaded with the lowest Q section, then the next section is cascaded with the next lowest Q section, and so on. Each pair of second order sections can then be improved upon by replacing it with a single section of fourth order. An example of a tenth order active filter using two fourth order sections and one second order section employing this technique is shown in Fig. 5.13.

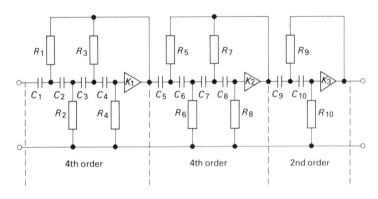

Fig. 5.13

The cascade scheme has the advantage that the individual stages can be built, tested and adjusted before being assembled together. However, the cascade design method is accompanied by lower sensitivity characteristics compared with a single block scheme such as that offered by the simulation of *LC* ladder structures.

One attempt to simulate the internal interactions present in an *LC* ladder network is to couple second-order stages through the use of negative feedback. This makes each natural mode dependent on more than one second-order stage and therefore, hopefully, less sensitive to variations in a single second-order stage.

5.7   Sensitivity

One of the main problems associated with active filters is the effect of component variations on the overall response of the filter. The effect is usually expressed quantitatively as the *sensitivity* of the filter relative to some component value. Sensitivity is therefore a measure of these changes which are due to variations in resistance, capacitance or amplifier gain. As a consequence, some circuit designs are considered as sensitive to even small component changes, while other circuits are regarded as relatively insensitive to small component changes.

A commonly used definition of the sensitivity of a function $F(s)$ is given by

$$S_x^{F(s)} \triangleq \frac{\delta F(s)/F(s)}{\delta x/x} \simeq \frac{\partial F(s)}{\partial x} \frac{x}{F(s)}$$

where x is the incremental variation in the component value x. In practice, particularly for second-order active filters, other sensitivity functions are also defined, as for example, the Q-sensitivity S_x^Q and the pole frequency sensitivity $S_x^{\omega_p}$ which are given respectively by

$$S_x^Q \triangleq \frac{\delta Q/Q}{\delta x/x} \simeq \frac{x}{Q} \frac{\partial Q}{\partial x}$$

$$S_x^{\omega_p} \triangleq \frac{\delta \omega_p/\omega_p}{\delta x/x} \simeq \frac{x}{\omega_p} \frac{\partial \omega_p}{\partial x}$$

where x is the component value subject to a variation δx, Q is the quality factor and ω_p is the pole frequency.

The importance of sensitivity is due to the fact that it relates a per unit change in component value to the resulting per unit change in overall circuit parameter. As an example, we have

$$\frac{\delta \omega_p}{\omega_p} \simeq S_x^{\omega_p} \frac{\delta x}{x}$$

where $\delta \omega_p$ is a small finite change in ω_p due to a small change δx in the component value x. This expression is only approximate but for the small tolerance limits specified for filters it provides a good approximation to the exact result. Hence, we observe that the ratio $\delta \omega_p/\omega_p$ is small if either $S_x^{\omega_p}$ is low or the ratio $\delta x/x$ is small. The latter condition implies very close tolerance components which can be expensive and so in practice a low value of sensitivity $S_x^{\omega_p}$ is highly desirable. Thus, the lower the sensitivity involved, the greater is the permissible component tolerance.

The sensitivity functions defined above involve partial derivatives. This is because the overall parameters are usually functions of various component values and in computing a possible change, the effects in the changes of all these components must be considered. This has naturally led to the definition of total sensitivity functions which are formed as a summation of the individual sensitivities or functions of time. One such total sensitivity function $S_T^{F(s)}$ for a set of elements $x_1, x_2 \ldots x_n$ is defined by the expression

$$S_T^{F(s)} = \sum_{i=1}^{i=n} S_{x_i}^{F(s)}$$

Example 5.2

In the Sallen and Key circuit shown in Fig. 5.10, obtain expressions for the sensitivities $S_{R_1}^{\omega_p}$, $S_{C_1}^{\omega_p}$ and S_K^Q. Hence, determine their values when $R_1 = R = 1\,\Omega$ and $C_1 = C_2 = 1\,\text{F}$. Comment on the results obtained.

Solution

The second-order transfer function for the circuit in Fig. 5.10 can be written in the form

$$H(s) = \frac{K}{s^2 + (\omega_p/Q)s + \omega_p^2}$$

Comparing this expression with the previous expression obtained for $H(s)$ in Example 5.1 yields

$$\omega_p = \frac{1}{\sqrt{R_1 R_2 C_1 C_2}}$$

and

$$Q = \frac{\sqrt{R_1 R_2 C_1 C_2}}{(R_1 + R_2)C_2 + R_1 C_1(1-K)}$$

The ω_p sensitivity for any component parameter x is defined by

$$S_x^{\omega_p} = \frac{x}{\omega_p}\frac{\partial \omega_p}{\partial x}$$

and so for $x = R_1$ we obtain

$$S_{R_1}^{\omega_p} = \frac{R_1 \sqrt{R_1 R_2 C_1 C_2}\,(-\tfrac{1}{2}R_1^{-3/2})}{\sqrt{R_2 C_1 C_2}} = -1/2$$

and for $x = C_1$ we obtain

$$S_{C_1}^{\omega_p} = \frac{C_1 \sqrt{R_1 R_2 C_1 C_2}\,(-\tfrac{1}{2}C_1^{-3/2})}{\sqrt{R_1 R_2 C_2}} = -1/2$$

The Q-sensitivity with respect to any circuit parameter x is defined by

$$S_x^Q = \frac{x}{Q}\frac{\partial Q}{\partial x}$$

and so for $x = K$ the gain parameter, we have

$$S_K^Q = \frac{K}{Q}\left\{\frac{-\sqrt{R_1 R_2 C_1 C_2}\,(-R_1 C_1)}{[(R_1+R_2)C_2 + R_1 C_1(1-K)]^2}\right\}$$

$$= \frac{K}{Q}\left\{\frac{R_1 C_1 \sqrt{R_1 R_2 C_1 C_2}}{[(R_1+R_2)C_2 + R_1 C_1(1-K)^2}\right\}$$

or

$$S_K^Q = \frac{KR_1 C_1}{[(R_1+R_2)C_2 + R_1 C_1(1-K)]}$$

When $R_1 = R_2 = 1\,\Omega$ and $C_1 = C_2 = 1\,F$ this yields

$$S_{R_1}^{\omega_p} = S_{C_1}^{\omega_p} = -1/2$$

and

$$S_K^Q = \frac{K}{(3-K)}$$

Comments
1. The ω_p sensitivities are equal and independent of the component values of R_1 and C_1.
2. The Q-sensitivity is low for small values of K e.g. when $K = 1$ (unity gain amplifier), $S_K^Q = 1/2$. The corresponding value of Q is also low as $Q = 1/2$.
3. If $K \simeq 3$ i.e. the positive feedback is increased, S_K^Q tends to a large value and so does Q. The circuit now becomes unstable.
4. Active filters designed with the Sallen and Key circuit are confined to low values of K and Q.

Example 5.3
The pole sensitivity with respect to any circuit parameter x is given by the expression

$$S_x^{p_i} = \frac{\partial p_i}{\partial x/x} = x\frac{\partial p_i}{\partial x}$$

where p_i is the ith pole in the denominator polynomial of the transfer function of an active filter. Hence, for the circuit shown in Fig. 5.14, evaluate the pole sensitivity when $K = 3$ and the pole displacement for a 1% increase in the value of K.

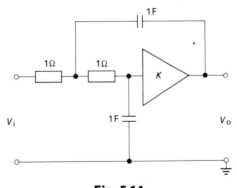

Fig. 5.14

Solution
For the circuit shown above, we have

$$\omega_p = \frac{1}{\sqrt{R_1 R_2 C_1 C_2}} = \frac{1}{\sqrt{1}} = 1$$

$$Q = \frac{\sqrt{R_1 R_2 C_1 C_2}}{(R_1 + R_2)C_2 + R_1 C_1 (1-K)} = \frac{1}{(2+1-K)}$$

or
$$Q = \frac{1}{(3-K)}$$

with
$$H(s) = \frac{K}{s^2 + (3-K)s + 1}$$

or
$$H(s) = \frac{3}{s^2 + 1} = \frac{3}{(s+j)(s-j)}$$

when $K = 3$. The ith poles are given by
$$p_i = \pm j$$

More generally, the ith poles for any value of K are given by the expression
$$p_i = \frac{-(3-K) \pm \sqrt{(3-K)^2 - 4}}{2}$$

or
$$p_i = \frac{-(3-K) \pm \sqrt{5 - 6K + K^2}}{2}$$

with
$$\frac{\partial p_i}{\partial K} = \tfrac{1}{2} \left[-(-1) \pm 0\cdot 5 \, (5 - 6K + K^2)^{-1/2} \, (-6 + 2K) \right]$$

or
$$\frac{\partial p_i}{\partial K} = 0\cdot 5 \pm (5 - 6K + K^2)^{-1/2} \, (-1\cdot 5 + 0\cdot 5 \, K)$$

For $K = 3$, $\dfrac{\partial p_i}{\partial K} = 0\cdot 5$ and we obtain
$$S_K^{p_i} = K \frac{\partial p_i}{\partial K}\bigg|_{K=3} = 3 \times 0\cdot 5 = 1\cdot 5$$

For a 1 % increase in the value of K, $\delta K = 0\cdot 03$ and we obtain for the pole displacement ∂p_i the value
$$\partial p_i = \frac{\partial K}{K} \, S_K^{p_i} = \frac{0\cdot 03}{3} \times 1\cdot 5 = 0\cdot 015$$

The new pole positions obtained are $p_i = \partial p_i \pm j = 0\cdot 015 \pm j$. These occur in the right half s-plane and so the circuit becomes unstable as mentioned earlier.

6
Digital filters

Analogue signals have been filtered by analogue filters for various purposes using well-known design techniques, but with the continued use of digital signals, digital signal processing is now being increasingly employed, using digital filters for filtering purposes.

A digital filter, in one sense, is essentially a *circuit* for converting a series of signal samples of an incoming digital signal into another series of signal samples as the outgoing digital signal. The signal samples, however, can also be in the form of pure binary numbers and so in another sense, a digital filter is a *technique* for converting one series of binary numbers into another prescribed series of binary numbers by processing it through a digital filter.

Digital filtering can therefore be performed entirely by means of *software* in the form of a computer program (algorithm). Originally, a large scale computer was used extensively as a digital filter, for achieving the required signal processing. At present, however, with the advances in integrated circuit technology (medium scale and large scale), digital filters can also be implemented using *hardware* in the form of adders, multipliers and shift registers, all of which can be integrated into the form of a single chip circuit.

As a consequence, the cost and complexity of implementing digital filters has been considerably reduced. Moreover, the considerable advantages of using digital filters such as compatibility, flexibility and stability, are likely to increase the use of digital filters in many applications dominated solely by analogue filters. However, digital filters do have their limitations. As digital signals are essentially quantised signal samples, quantisation leads to errors which depend on the number of bits used to represent each signal sample. The quantisation, therefore, determines the accuracy or quality of the filtering process which in another sense can be regarded as an increase in 'quantisation noise'. Further noise is also due to 'round off' errors associated with multipliers used in digital filters.

6.1 Filter designs[40-44]

The two main types of digital filters are the *infinite-impulse* response or IIR filter and the *finite-impulse* response or FIR filter. Digital filters may also be classified as *recursive* or *non-recursive* filters according to the manner in which they are realised. Recursive filters employ structures with feed forward and feedback present and are easily implemented as IIR filters.

Non-recursive filters employ structures with only feedforward present and are usually implemented as FIR filters.

The general technique used for designing such filters is closely associated with those used for analogue filters. Since the essential task of a filter is for filtering purposes, the frequency characteristics are chosen first, and the corresponding analogue filter design which achieves this closely is obtained. The method used for this involves an s-plane analysis and the well-known rational functions for Butterworth filters, Chebyshev filters etc.

To obtain the corresponding digital filter, it is necessary to proceed to a z-plane analysis by means of the z-transform. The digital filter design is then a simple 'mapping' operation from the s-plane to the z-plane which involves the use of both polynomial and rational functions of the parameter $z = e^{sT}$ where $s = j\omega$ and T is the sampling period. Figs. 6.1 and 6.2 illustrate examples of recursive and non-recursive structures respectively.

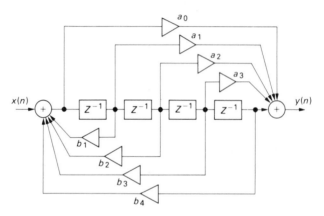

Fig. 6.1   Recursive filter (4th order)

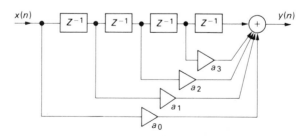

Fig. 6.2   Non-recursive filter (4th order)

6.2 The z-transform[45]

In discrete-time or digital systems, the z-transform may be used just as the Laplace transform is applied in continuous-time or analogue systems. There are many similarities between the two transforms since the z-parameter is a complex variable like the s-parameter. However, instead of the integration employed in the Laplace transform, a summation is used in the z-transform. The one-sided z-transform of a sequence of samples of a digital signal $x(t)$ is defined by

$$X(z) = \sum_{n=0}^{n=\infty} x(n)z^{-n}$$

where $z = e^{sT} = e^{j\omega T}$ and z^{-n} signifies a delay factor, while $x(n)$ are the various discrete values of the input signal samples of $x(t)$ such as $x(1)$, $x(2)$, etc . . . , which are spaced at intervals of time T.

To assist in the application of the z-transform to filter problems, it is necessary to be acquainted with the standard transform functions and operations which are summarised respectively in Tables 6.1 and 6.2.

Table 6.1

$x(n)$	$X(z)$
$\delta(n)$	1
1	$\dfrac{z}{(z-1)}$
nT	$\dfrac{zT}{(z-1)^2}$
e^{-naT} (a is constant)	$\dfrac{z}{(z-e^{-aT})}$
a^n	$\dfrac{z}{(z-a)}$
$\sin naT$	$\dfrac{z\sin aT}{(z^2-2z\cos aT+1)}$
$\cos naT$	$\dfrac{(z^2-z\cos aT)}{(z^2-2z\cos aT+1)}$

Example 6.1
Obtain the z-transform of the step-function $u(n)$ defined by

$$u(n) = 0 \quad \text{for } n < 0$$
$$u(n) = 1 \quad \text{for } n > 0$$

when z is a complex variable with $|z| > 1$.

Table 6.2

$x(n)$	$X(z)$
$x(n+1)$	$zX(z) - zX(0)$
$nx(n)$	$-z\dfrac{d}{dz}[X(z)]$
$a^n x(n)$	$X(z/a)$
$\displaystyle\sum_{n=0}^{n=\infty} x(n)$	$\dfrac{z}{(z-1)}[X(z)]$
$\displaystyle\sum_{k=0}^{k=\infty} x_2(k)x_1(n-k)$	$X_1(z)X_2(z)$

Solution
Here

$$X(z) = \sum_{n=0}^{n=\infty} f(n)z^{-n}$$

or

$$X(z) = \sum_{n=0}^{n=\infty} 1.z^{-n}$$

with

$$X(z) = \frac{1}{z^0} + \frac{1}{z^1} + \frac{1}{z^2}$$

For $|z| > 1$, this yields a convergent geometrical series whose sum $X(z)$ is given by

$$X(z) = 1 - (1/z)^\infty/(1 - 1/z) = \frac{1}{[1 - 1/z]}$$

or

$$X(z) = z/(z-1)$$

Comment
The z-transform is ideally suited for finding low-pass and band-pass digital filters. It is particularly suited to continuous filters derived from all-pole low-pass Butterworth, Bessel and Chebyshev designs.

6.3   Inverse z-transform

To obtain $x(n)$ from $X(z)$, the inverse z-transform is required. This can be obtained in three ways. In the first method, the z-transform is found with a contour integral thus

$$x(n) = \frac{1}{2\pi j} \oint X(z)z^{n-1} \, dz$$

and the path of integration is a unit circle in the z-plane.

In the second method, $X(z)$ is expressed as a power series and the values of $x(n)$ are then obtained from standard tables.

The third method, which is the most practical one, expresses $X(z)$ in terms of partial fractions which are then identified from standard tables. This method is very similar to the one used for finding the inverse Laplace transform.

Example 6.2

Derive the inverse z-transform of the function $X(z)$ given by

$$X(z) = \frac{1}{1 - 3z^{-1} + 2z^{-2}}$$

Solution

$$X(z) = \frac{z^2}{z^2 - 3z + 2}$$

or

$$\frac{X(z)}{z} = \frac{z}{(z-2)(z-1)}$$

By using a partial fraction expansion we obtain

$$\frac{z}{(z-2)(z-1)} = \frac{A}{(z-2)} + \frac{B}{(z-1)}$$

or

$$z \equiv A(z-1) + B(z-2)$$

Equating the coefficient of z and the constant term on both sides yields

$$1 = A + B$$
$$0 = -A - 2B$$

Hence

$$A = -2B$$

with

$$1 = -2B + B$$

or

$$B = -1, A = 2$$

Thus

$$X(z)/z = 2/(z-2) - 1/(z-1)$$

or

$$X(z) = \frac{2z}{(z-2)} - \frac{z}{(z-1)}$$

with

$$x(n) = 2(2)^n - 1$$

6.4 Transfer functions

For any time-invariant linear filter, if $x(n)$ and $y(n)$ are the input and output sequences, the transfer function $H(z)$ of the filter is defined as the ratio of $Y(z)$ to $X(z)$ where $X(z)$, $Y(z)$ are the z-transforms of $x(n)$ and $y(n)$ respectively. This is illustrated in Fig. 6.3.

Fig. 6.3

We have

$$H(z) = \frac{Y(z)}{X(z)}$$

or

$$Y(z) = H(z)X(z)$$

as the above result follows directly by means of the convolution integral. Furthermore, if $X(z)$ is the z-transform of a unit impulse sequence, then $X(z) = 1$ and $H(z) = Y(z)$ i.e. the transfer function $H(z)$ is just the z-transform of the impulse response of the filter.

In general, $X(z)$ and $Y(z)$ may be polynomials and so $H(z)$ is of the form

$$H(z) = \frac{Y(z)}{X(z)} = \frac{a_0 + a_1 z^{-1} + \ldots}{1 + b_1 z^{-1} + \ldots}$$

which can also be expressed in terms of poles and zeros in the form

$$H(z) = \frac{K(z^{-1} - z_1)(z^{-1} - z_2) \ldots}{(1 - p_1 z^{-1})(1 - p_2 z^{-1}) \ldots}$$

or

$$H(z) = \frac{K \prod_{i=1}^{i=N} (z^{-1} - z_i)}{\prod_{j=1}^{j=N} (1 - p_j z^{-1})}$$

where K is a constant, z_i are the zeros and p_j are the poles which are located on the z-plane. The relationship $z = e^{sT}$ leads to a mapping of poles and zeros from the s-plane to those in the z-plane and is illustrated in Fig. 6.4.

From Fig. 6.4 it will be observed that poles exist in the left hand s-plane only from stability considerations. By virtue of the relationship $z = e^{sT}$, the ω-axis maps over into the unit circle with stable poles lying in the region *inside* the unit circle. Furthermore, it will be observed that the pole-zero pattern is *periodic* in the z-plane and so the frequency response of the digital filter exhibits this periodicity at intervals of $1/T$ or at a frequency $\omega = 2\pi/T$, where T is the sampling period. This is a direct consequence of the sampling feature of the digital signal.

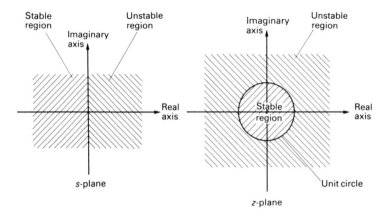

Fig. 6.4

6.5 Infinite-impulse response filter (IIR filter)

An IIR filter is characterized by an impulse response $h(n)$ which consists of an infinite number of samples. Thus, $h(n)$ is non-zero in the range $0 \leqslant n \leqslant \infty$. It is represented by a transfer function of the form

$$H(z) = \frac{\sum\limits_{i=0}^{i=m} a_i z^{-i}}{\sum\limits_{j=0}^{j=n} b_j z^{-j}}$$

where a_i are the coefficients which define the zeros and b_j are the coefficients which define the poles of the transfer function.

The IIR filter is stable if all the poles of $H(z)$ lie within the unit circle in the *z-plane*. Usually $b_0 = 1$ for a causal filter and so the general transfer function is given by

$$H(z) = \frac{\sum\limits_{i=0}^{i=m} a_i z^{-i}}{1 + \sum\limits_{j=1}^{j=n} b_j z^{-j}}$$

Because of the similarities between the transfer functions of IIR filters and analogue filters, it is convenient first to design the analogue filter which meets the required specifications and then to derive, by mapping techniques, the design of the corresponding digital filter. Hence, this filter can lead to the well-known designs for low-pass, high-pass and band-pass filters, using the rational functions associated with Butterworth, Chebyshev or elliptic function filter designs. Two important mapping techniques used for designing such filters are the *bilinear transformation* and the *impulse-invariant transformation*.

(a) Bilinear transformation

This is one of the best procedures for designing IIR filters with respect to the corresponding analogue filters in terms of frequency response similarity and simplicity of design. It is a one-to-one continuous mapping procedure from the s-plane to the z-plane i.e. it maps periodic sections of the s-plane along the entire $j\omega$ axis on to the unit circle in the z-plane. The mapping is periodic with multiples of the sampling frequency $f_s = 1/T$. The transformation is defined by

$$s = f(z) \triangleq \frac{2}{T} \frac{(1 - z^{-1})}{(1 + z^{-1})}$$

or

$$j\omega = \frac{2}{T} \frac{(1 - e^{-j\omega T})}{(1 + e^{-j\omega T})}$$

with

$$\omega = \frac{2}{jT} \frac{(1 - e^{-j\omega T})}{(1 + e^{-j\omega T})} = \frac{2}{T} \tan \frac{\omega T}{2}$$

and so the frequencies in the s-plane are related to frequencies in the z-plane by the relationship

$$f_s = \frac{1}{\pi T} \tan (\pi f_z T)$$

or

$$\omega_s = \frac{2}{T} \tan (\omega_z T / 2)$$

Due to the tangent function, the frequency response is considerably compressed on the frequency scale of the digital filter. This is known as *frequency warping* and is illustrated in Fig. 6.5. However, the transformation preserves the magnitude scaling of the analogue filter e.g. an equi-ripple analogue filter after transformation is still an equi-ripple digital filter. The corresponding transfer function is obtained by simple substitution of s for z in the transfer function and is given by

$$H(s) \rightarrow H\left[\frac{2}{T}\left(\frac{1 - z^{-1}}{1 + z^{-1}}\right)\right] = H(z)$$

Comment

The bilinear transformation is particularly suited to the design of high-pass and band-stop filters with desired frequency characteristics.

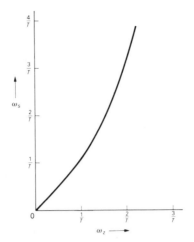

Fig. 6.5

(b)   Impulse-invariant transformation

A digital filter can be designed to have frequency characteristics similar to those of a given analogue filter, if the impulse response of the digital filter is a sampled version of the impulse response of the analogue filter. As the impulse response is *invariant* by this procedure, the method is known as the impulse invariant transformation.

The basic procedure is to obtain initially the transfer function $H(s)$ of the analogue filter in the form

$$H(s) = \sum_{i=1}^{i=m} \frac{g_i}{(s+p_i)}$$

where g_i is a gain factor and p_i is the ith pole of the analogue filter. Its impulse response $h(t)$ is then given by using the inverse Laplace transform which yields

$$h(t) = \mathscr{L}^{-1}\left[H(s)\right]$$

or

$$h(t) = \sum_{i=1}^{i=m} g_i e^{-p_i t}$$

If $h(n)$ is the impulse response of the equivalent digital filter, we have by definition

$$h(n) \triangleq h(t)\big|_{t=nT}$$

or

$$h(n) = h(nT)$$

where T is the sampling period. The transfer function $H(z)$ of the digital filter is now easily obtained from the relationship

$$H(z) = \sum_{n=1}^{n=\infty} h(n)z^{-n}$$

where

$$h(n) = \sum_{i=1}^{i=m} g_i e^{-p_i nT}$$

Hence, substituting for $h(n)$ then yields

$$H(z) = \sum_{i=1}^{i=m} \sum_{n=1}^{n=\infty} g_i e^{-p_i nT} z^{-n}$$

or

$$H(z) = \sum_{i=1}^{i=m} \frac{g_i}{(1 - z^{-1} e^{-p_i T})}$$

By comparing the expressions for $H(z)$ and $H(s)$, we observe that $H(z)$ is easily obtained from $H(s)$ by replacing the factor $[1/(s + p_i)]$ by the factor $[1/(1 - z^{-1} e^{-p_i T})]$.

Example 6.3
A maximally flat response digital filter has the following specifications:

(a) pass-band attenuation $< 3\,\text{dB}$ from 0 to 3 kHz;
(b) stop-band attenuation $> 12\,\text{dB}$ at 6 kHz;
(c) sampling frequency $= 30\,\text{kHz}$.

Obtain an expression for the transfer function of the digital filter using the bilinear transformation method.

Solution
The low-pass digital filter cut-off frequency ω_c is given by

$$\omega_c = 2\pi \times 3 \times 10^3 = 6\pi \times 10^3 \text{ rads/s}$$

with

$$\omega_c T = \frac{6\pi \times 10^3 \times 1}{30 \times 10^3} = 0{\cdot}2\,\pi \text{ rads}$$

where T is the sampling period.
The stop-band frequency ω_f is given by

$$\omega_f = 2\pi \times 6 \times 10^3 = 12\pi \times 10^3 \text{ rads/s}$$

with

$$\omega_f T = \frac{12\pi \times 10^3}{30 \times 10^3} = 0{\cdot}4\,\pi \text{ rads}$$

The corresponding frequencies for an analogue filter are

$$\omega_c = k \tan(0{\cdot}2\,\pi/2) = 0{\cdot}3249\,k$$

$$\omega_f = k \tan(0{\cdot}4\,\pi/2) = 0{\cdot}7265\,k$$

where $k = 2/T$ is a design constant.

For a maximally flat response we require a Butterworth filter of order n with a transfer function

$$H(s) = \frac{1}{\sqrt{1 + (\omega_f/\omega_c)^{2n}}}$$

with

$$20 \log_{10} \frac{1}{\sqrt{1 + (\omega_f/\omega_c)^{2n}}} > -12$$

or

$$\log_{10}[1 + (\omega_f/\omega_c)^{2n}] > 1\cdot2$$

Substituting for (ω_f/ω_c) from above yields

$$\left[\frac{0\cdot7265\,k}{0\cdot3249\,k}\right]^{2n} > 14\cdot85$$

or

$$n > 1\cdot676$$

A second-order Butterworth filter is required with poles s_1, s_2 normalised for $\omega_c = 0\cdot3249\,k$. Hence, we obtain

$$H(s) = \frac{1}{(s + s_1)(s + s_2)} = \frac{1}{s^2 + s(s_1 + s_2) + s_1 s_2}$$

where

$$s_1 = \omega_c(0\cdot707 + j0\cdot707) = (0\cdot2297 + j0\cdot2297)\,k$$

and

$$s_2 = \omega_c(0\cdot707 - j0\cdot707) = (0\cdot2297 - j0\cdot2297)\,k$$

and if $H(s)$ is normalised to unity gain at $s = 0$ we obtain

$$H(s) = \frac{0\cdot1055\,k^2}{s^2 + s(0\cdot4594\,k) + 0\cdot1055\,k^2}$$

The digital filter transfer function $H(z)$ is obtained by using the substitution

$$s = \frac{2}{T}\left(\frac{1 - z^{-1}}{1 + z^{-1}}\right) = k\left(\frac{z-1}{z+1}\right)$$

Hence

$$H(z) = \frac{0\cdot1055\,k^2}{k^2\left(\dfrac{z-1}{z+1}\right)^2 + \left(\dfrac{z-1}{z+1}\right)(0\cdot4594)k^2 + 0\cdot1055\,k^2}$$

with

$$H(z) = \frac{0\cdot1055\,(z^2 + 2z + 1)}{(z-1)^2 + (z^2 - 1)(0\cdot4594) + (z+1)^2(0\cdot1055)}$$

and

$$H(z) = \frac{0\cdot1055\,(z^2 + 2z + 1)}{1\cdot5649\,z^2 - 1\cdot789\,z + 0\cdot6461}$$

or

$$H(z) = \frac{(1 + 2z^{-1} + z^{-2})}{14\cdot833 - 16\cdot957\,z^{-1} + 6\cdot1242\,z^{-2}}$$

6.6 Frequency transformations

From a low-pass digital filter design with a cut-off frequency ω_c, other filter configurations may be designed such as high-pass, band-pass and band-stop by replacing the parameter z with the corresponding bilinear transformations summarised in Table 6.3.

Table 6.3

Transformation	Parameters
High-pass	ω_c = low-pass cut-off frequency
$$-\left[\frac{z^{-1}+\alpha}{1+\alpha z^{-1}}\right]$$	ω_h = high-pass cut-off frequency
	$$\alpha = -\frac{\cos\left[(\omega_c-\omega_h)T/2\right]}{\cos\left[(\omega_c+\omega_h)T/2\right]}$$
Band-pass	ω_l = lower cut-off frequency
$$-\frac{\left[z^{-2}-\left(\frac{2\alpha\beta}{\beta+1}\right)z^{-1}+\left(\frac{\beta-1}{\beta+1}\right)\right]}{\left[\left(\frac{\beta-1}{\beta+1}\right)z^{-2}-\left(\frac{2\alpha\beta}{\beta+1}\right)z^{-1}+1\right]}$$	ω_u = upper cut-off frequency
	$$\alpha = \frac{\cos\left[(\omega_u+\omega_l)T/2\right]}{\cos\left[(\omega_u-\omega_l)T/2\right]}$$
	$$\beta = \cot\left[(\omega_u-\omega_l)T/2\right]\tan\left(\frac{\omega_c T}{2}\right)$$
Band-stop	ω_l = lower cut-off frequency
$$\frac{\left[z^{-2}-\left(\frac{2\alpha}{1+\beta}\right)z^{-1}+\left(\frac{1-\beta}{1+\beta}\right)\right]}{\left[\left(\frac{1-\beta}{1+\beta}\right)z^{-2}-\left(\frac{2\alpha\beta}{1+\beta}\right)z^{-1}+1\right]}$$	ω_u = upper cut-off frequency
	$$\alpha = \frac{\cos\left[(\omega_u+\omega_l)T/2\right]}{\cos\left[(\omega_u-\omega_l)T/2\right]}$$
	$$\beta = \tan\left[(\omega_u-\omega_l)T/2\right]\tan\left(\frac{\omega_c T}{2}\right)$$

6.7   Finite-impulse response filters (FIR filters)

Finite-impulse response filters or non-recursive filters have a number of advantages such as the possibility of a linear phase characteristic and a stability of operation is assured. However, the disadvantages are that an extra provision for storage and a greater number of arithmetic operations are required compared to IIR filters. Two well-known techniques for designing such filters are the *Fourier series* method and the *frequency sampling* method.

(a)   Fourier series method
The frequency response $H(e^{j\theta})$ of any digital filter is a periodic function of $\theta = \omega T$ and it can be expanded as a Fourier series in the form

$$He^{j\theta} = \sum_{n=-\infty}^{n=\infty} h(n)e^{-jn\theta}$$

with

$$h(n) = \frac{1}{2\pi}\int_0^{2\pi}(He^{j\theta})e^{jn\theta}\,d\theta$$

where the Fourier series coefficients $h(n)$ represent the impulse response sequence of the digital filter.

This leads to an infinite series summation which may be truncated after N terms to obtain a finite number of terms for an FIR filter. However, the truncation leads to overshoots and ripples in the frequency response due to the Gibb's phenomenon[41] which may be troublesome. To overcome these effects, additional weighting is applied to the series coefficients $h(n)$ by means of a 'window' function such that the finite truncated value $h_T(n)$ is now given by

$$h_T(n) = h(n)w(n)$$

where $w(n)$ is the window function employed. It has the effect of smoothing the magnitude response and involves multiplication in the time domain or convolving the desired frequency response with the Fourier transform of the 'window' function in the frequency domain. To achieve various effects, several window functions $w(n)$ with their Fourier transforms $W(f)$ are given below and illustrated in Fig. 6.6.

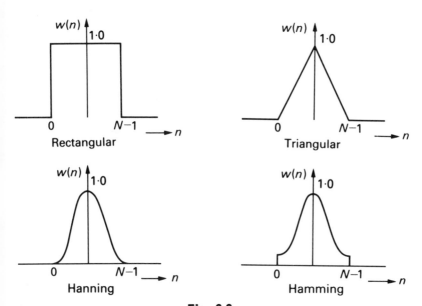

Fig. 6.6

Rectangular window

$$w(n) = 1 \qquad \text{for } 0 \leqslant n \leqslant N-1$$
$$= 0 \qquad \text{elsewhere}$$
$$W(f) = \frac{(N-1)\sin\{\pi f(N-1)\}}{\pi f(N-1)}$$

Triangular window

$$w(n) = \frac{2n}{N-1} \qquad \text{for } 0 \leqslant n \leqslant \frac{N-1}{2}$$

$$= 2 - \frac{2n}{N-1} \qquad \text{for } \frac{N-1}{2} \leqslant n \leqslant N-1$$

$$= 0 \qquad\qquad \text{elsewhere}$$

$$W(f) = \left(\frac{N-1}{2}\right)\left[\frac{\sin\{\pi f(N-1)/2\}}{\pi f(N-1)/2}\right]^2$$

Hanning window

$$w(n) = \frac{1}{2}\left[1 - \cos\left(\frac{2\pi n}{N-1}\right)\right] \qquad \text{for } 0 \leqslant n \leqslant N-1$$

$$= 0 \qquad\qquad \text{elsewhere}$$

$$W(f) = \left(\frac{N-1}{2}\right)\frac{\sin\{\pi f(N-1)\}}{\pi f(N-1)}\left[\frac{1}{1 - \{f(N-1)\}^2}\right]$$

Hamming window

$$w(n) = 0{\cdot}54 - 0{\cdot}46 \cos\left(\frac{2\pi n}{N-1}\right) \qquad 0 \leqslant n \leqslant N-1$$

$$= 0 \qquad\qquad \text{elsewhere}$$

$$W(f) = \frac{(N-1)\sin\{\pi f(N-1)\}}{\pi f(N-1)}\left[\frac{0{\cdot}54 - 0{\cdot}08\{f(N-1)\}^2}{1 - \{f(N-1)\}^2}\right]$$

where N is even.

The transfer function $H(z)$ of the FIR filter can be obtained by substituting z for $e^{j\theta}$ in the expression for $He^{j\theta}$. Thus, we have

$$H(z) = \sum_{n=-\infty}^{n=\infty} h(n)z^{-n} = \sum_{n=0}^{n=N-1} h_T(n)z^{-n}$$

or

$$H(z) = h_0 + h_1 z^{-1} + h_2 z^{-2} \ldots h_{N-1}z^{N-1}$$

where the impulse response $h(n)$ is terminated after N terms and consists of N finite samples only. A typical implementation of this filter is known as a transversal filter and is illustrated in Fig. 6.7.

The analogue input signal $x(t)$ is sampled and quantised in digital form as a binary number by an A/D converter. An N-stage shift register operating as a delay network holds successive numbers and shifts the sequence one stage on receiving a clock pulse every T seconds.

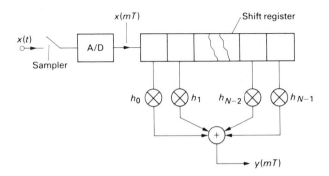

Fig. 6.7

The output number sequence $y(mT)$ for an input number sequence $x(mT)$ is given by

$$y(mT) = \sum_{n=0}^{n=N-1} h_T(n)x(m-n)T$$

where $h_T(n)$ are the weighted coefficients corresponding to the frequency characteristic required. The accuracy of the output sequence is determined by the number of bits employed for each binary number and on the digital multiplication which involves 'round off' errors in the binary arithmetic.

A special feature of an FIR filter, as mentioned before, is its linear phase characteristic which is determined by the phase angle of the response function $He^{j\theta}$. It is given by $\varphi(\theta) = [(N-1)/2]\theta$ where $-\pi < \theta < +\pi$ and as a consequence, such filters can be used for equalising group delay characteristics in long distance transmission lines.

(b) Frequency sampling method
An FIR filter can be represented by a discrete Fourier transform (DFT) series denoted by $H(m)$ or in terms of its impulse response coefficients denoted by $h(n)$, by means of the following expressions

$$H(m) = \sum_{n=0}^{n=N-1} h(n)e^{-j\left(\frac{2\pi}{N}\right)mn}$$

and

$$h(n) = \frac{1}{N} \sum_{m=0}^{N-1} H(m)e^{j\left(\frac{2\pi}{N}\right)mn}$$

since the DFT series $H(m)$ can be regarded as numerical samples of the filter's z-transform, evaluated at N equally spaced points on the unit circle in the z-plane. Thus, we have

$$H(m) = H(z)\big|_{z=e^{j\left(\frac{2\pi}{N}\right)m}}$$

with
$$H(z) = \sum_{n=0}^{N-1} h(n)z^{-n} = \sum_{n=0}^{N-1} \left[\frac{1}{N} \sum_{m=0}^{N-1} H(m) e^{j\left(\frac{2\pi}{N}\right)mn} z^{-n} \right]$$

or
$$H(z) = \sum_{m=0}^{N-1} \frac{H(m)}{N} \sum_{n=0}^{N-1} e^{j\left(\frac{2\pi}{N}\right)mn} z^{-n}$$

$$= \sum_{m=0}^{N-1} \frac{H(m)}{N} \left[\frac{1 - e^{j2\pi m} z^{-N}}{1 - z^{-1} e^{j\left(\frac{2\pi}{N}\right)m}} \right]$$

and as $e^{j2\pi m} = 1$ we obtain

$$H(z) = \frac{1}{N} \sum_{m=0}^{N-1} \frac{H(m)(1 - z^{-N})}{[1 - z^{-1} e^{j\left(\frac{2\pi}{N}\right)m}]}$$

which represents the transfer function of an FIR filter whose frequency response corresponds exactly to those of the required values at the sampled points given by $\theta = (2\pi m/N)$ where $m = 0, 1 \ldots (N-1)$. This is illustrated in Fig. 6.8 where it is shown that in between the sampled points, the response function may exhibit ripples due to the Gibb's phenomenon.

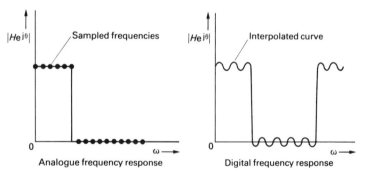

Analogue frequency response   Digital frequency response

Fig. 6.8

6.8 Quantisation effects

The implementation of digital filters involves the use of a finite number of bits to express their state and coefficient values. This fact produces several errors which are summarised as follows.

(a) Quantisation of the input analogue signal into a set of discrete levels in the A/D converter. The variance of this error is $\sigma^2 = q^2/12$ where q is the 'step' size of each level.

(b) Quantisation of the filter coefficients a_i and b_i into a finite number of bits.
(c) Quantisation of the results of arithmetic operations e.g. when the sum or product of two numbers exceed the number of bits available and are known as 'round off' errors.

The effects of these various errors lead to a form of quantisation 'noise' which can be reduced arbitrarily by choosing a word length (number of bits per word) sufficiently large, but this increases the time of operation and the cost of the digital filter.

Example 6.4
Design a low-pass FIR filter using the Fourier series method and a rectangular window function. The filter employs 10 delay sections with a cut-off frequency of 3 kHz and a sampling frequency of 10 kHz. Obtain an expression for the transfer function of the digital filter.

Solution
The ideal filter response is shown in Fig. 6.9 where f_c is the cut-off frequency and f_s is the sampling frequency. The Fourier coefficients $h(n)$ for the filter are given by

$$h(n) = \frac{1}{2\pi} \int_0^{2\pi} H e^{j\theta} e^{jn\theta} d\theta$$

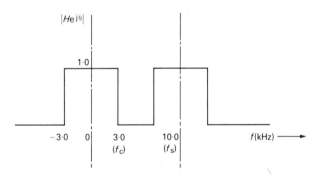

Fig. 6.9

For the symmetrical response function which is repetitive at the sampling frequency f_s as illustrated in Fig. 6.9, only cosine terms are required. Furthermore, with a rectangular window function we have $h_T(n) = h(n)$ and $|He^{j\theta}| = 1$. Thus

$$h(n) = \frac{1}{2\pi} \int_0^{2\pi} 1 \cdot \cos(n\theta) d\theta$$

or

$$h(n) \frac{1}{\pi} \int_0^{\pi} \cos(n\theta) d\theta$$

For a normalised value of $\theta_s = 2\pi$ we have

$$\frac{\theta_c}{\theta_s} = \frac{\omega_c T}{\omega_s T} = \frac{f_c}{f_s} = \frac{3 \times 10^3}{10 \times 10^3} = 0.3$$

with

$$\theta_c = 2\pi \times 0.3 = 0.6\pi.$$

Hence

$$h(n) = \frac{1}{\pi} \int_0^{\theta_c} \cos(n\theta)\, d\theta = \frac{1}{\pi} \left[\frac{\sin(n\theta)}{n} \right]_0^{0.6\pi}$$

or

$$h(n) = 0.6 \left[\frac{\sin n(0.6\pi)}{n(0.6\pi)} \right]$$

The transfer function of the digital filter is given by

$$H(z) = \sum_{n=-5}^{n=5} h(n)z^{-n} = \sum_{m=0}^{m=10} h(m)z^{-m}$$

where $m = (5 - n)$. The filter coefficients are obtained from symmetry as follows:

$$
\begin{aligned}
h(0) &= h(10) = 0.6 \times \quad 0 \quad\quad = \quad 0 \\
h(1) &= h(9) \ \ = 0.6 \times \quad 0.1262 = \quad 0.0757 \\
h(2) &= h(8) \ \ = 0.6 \times -0.1039 = -0.0624 \\
h(3) &= h(7) \ \ = 0.6 \times -0.2146 = -0.1288 \\
h(4) &= h(6) \ \ = 0.6 \times \quad 0.5046 = \quad 0.3028 \\
h(5) &\ \ \ = 0.6 \times \quad 1.0 \quad\quad = \quad 0.6
\end{aligned}
$$

Thus, we obtain

$$
\begin{aligned}
H(z) = \ &0.0757z^{-1} - 0.0624z^{-2} - 0.1288z^{-3} \\
&+ 0.3028z^{-4} + 0.6z^{-5} + 0.3028z^{-6} \\
&- 0.1288z^{-7} - 0.0624z^{-8} + 0.0757z^{-9}.
\end{aligned}
$$

6.9   Filter synthesis

In order to realise a given transfer function $H(z)$, two possible structures are available. They are known as the *series* form and the *parallel* form.

In the series or cascade form, $H(z)$ is expressed as the product of various first-order or second-order functions and the filter is synthesized by cascading the various sections as is illustrated in Fig. 6.10.

Fig. 6.10

Thus, we have

$$H(z) = H_1(z)H_2(z) \ldots H_n(z)$$

where $H_n(z)$ is of the form

$$H_n(z) = \frac{1 + a_1 z^{-1}}{1 + b_1 z^{-1}} \qquad \text{(first-order)}$$

or $\qquad H_n(z) = \frac{1 + a_1 z^{-1} + a_2 z^{-2}}{1 + b_1 z^{-1} + b_2 z^{-2}} \qquad \text{(second-order)}$

In the parallel form, $H(z)$ is expressed as the sum of various first-order or second-order functions and the filter is synthesized with a parallel combination of the various sections as is illustrated in Fig. 6.11.

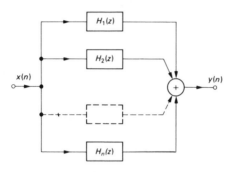

Fig. 6.11

Thus, we have

$$H(z) = H_1(z) + H_2(z) + \ldots H_n(z)$$

where $H_n(z)$ is of the form

$$H_n(z) = \frac{a_0}{1 + b_1 z^{-1}} \qquad \text{(first-order)}$$

or $\qquad H_n(z) = \frac{a_0 + a_1 z^{-1}}{1 + b_1 z^{-1} + b_2 z^{-2}} \qquad \text{(second-order)}$

Comment
To achieve other filter structures, various combinations of the series and parallel forms may be employed.

Example 6.5
Synthesize a parallel form of digital filter structure for the transfer function $H(z)$ given by

$$H(z) = \frac{z^2 + 0{\cdot}3z - 0{\cdot}04}{z^2 + 0{\cdot}1z - 0{\cdot}06}$$

Solution

We have

$$H(z) = \frac{z^2 + 0\cdot3z - 0\cdot04}{z^2 + 0\cdot1z - 0\cdot06} = \frac{(z - 0\cdot1)(z + 0\cdot4)}{(z - 0\cdot2)(z + 0\cdot3)}$$

or

$$\frac{H(z)}{z} = \frac{(z - 0\cdot1)(z + 0\cdot4)}{z(z - 0\cdot2)(z + 0\cdot3)} = \frac{A}{z} + \frac{B}{(z - 0\cdot2)} + \frac{C}{(z + 0\cdot3)}$$

Thus

$$z^2 + 0\cdot3z - 0\cdot04 \equiv A(z - 0\cdot2)(z + 0\cdot3) + Bz(z + 0\cdot3) + Cz(z - 0\cdot2)$$

with

$$1 = A + B + C$$

$$0\cdot3 = 0\cdot1A + 0\cdot3B - 0\cdot2C$$

$$-0\cdot04 = -0\cdot06A$$

Hence

$$A = 2/3$$

$$B = 3/5$$

$$C = -4/5$$

and

$$H(z) = 2/3 + \frac{(3/5)z}{(z - 0\cdot2)} + \frac{(-4/5)z}{(z + 0\cdot3)}$$

with

$$H_1(z) = 2/3$$

$$H_2(z) = \frac{(3/5)}{(1 - 0\cdot2z^{-1})}$$

$$H_3(z) = \frac{(-4/5)}{(1 + 0\cdot3z^{-1})}$$

and the parallel form of filter structure is shown in Fig. 6.12.

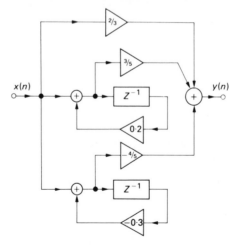

Fig. 6.12

Problems

1 A voltage is induced in a series circuit consisting of an inductance L, an effective resistance R of $12\,\Omega$ and a capacitance C. The Q-factor of the coil is 100 and the circuit is tuned to resonance at 1 MHz. Determine the ratio of the voltage across the capacitor at resonance to that across it at 10 kHz off resonance and the value of C.

2 Design a series Foster network to have a pole at $\omega = 10^6$ rad/s and a zero at $\omega = 2 \times 10^6$ rad/s. The impedance of the network is $j250\,\Omega$ at $\omega = 0.5 \times 10^6$ rad/s.

3 A reactance function has an internal zero at $\omega = 2 \times 10^6$ rad/s and an internal pole at $\omega = 10^7$ rad/s. The driving-point impedance is $j200\,\Omega$ at $\omega = 8 \times 10^6$ rad/s. Sketch the reactance curve and determine the first Foster network.

4 Synthesize the first Cauer network for the driving-point impedance function given by

$$Z(s) = \frac{2s^4 + 8s^2 + 6}{s^3 + 2s}$$

5 In Fig. 3.15(a), $R_1 = R_2 = \alpha R$ and $C_1 = C_2 = C$. If $R_3 = R$ and $C_3 = \alpha C$, what is the value of α if the output voltage V_o is zero? Determine the corresponding angular frequency ω_o of the input voltage V_i.

6 The reactance variation with frequency for a pure reactance network which is physically realisable is expressed by one of the three equations given below. Determine which one it is and explain why the other two equations are inappropriate.

(a) $X = \dfrac{j\omega(\omega^2 - 1)}{(\omega^2 - 4)(\omega^2 - 9)}$

(b) $X = \dfrac{-j\omega(\omega^2 - 4)}{(\omega^2 - 1)(\omega^2 - 9)}$

(c) $X = \dfrac{j(\omega^2 - 4)}{(\omega^2 - 1)(\omega^2 - 9)}$

7 Explain the terms *image impedance* and *iterative impedance* as applied to a two-port network.

In a two-port resistive T-network the series arm resistances are R_a and R_b, while the shunt arm resistance is R_c. The resistance measured at the input terminals is $750\,\Omega$ when the output terminals are open-circuited and $300\,\Omega$ when they are short-circuited. The resistance measured at the output terminals is $800\,\Omega$ when the input terminals are open-circuited.

Calculate the values of R_a, R_b and R_c, and the image impedances. Hence, determine the insertion loss produced by the network when inserted between its image impedances. (C.E.I.)

8   In the equivalent circuit shown in Fig. 3.13, $Z_1 = X_a$ and $Z_2 = X_b$, where X_a, X_b are pure reactance elements. Determine the characteristic impedance Z_0 for the symmetrical bridge network. Obtain an expression for the propagation coefficient γ in terms of X_a and X_b when the network is correctly terminated. If X_a and X_b are of opposite sign, show that the attenuation of the network is zero at all frequencies.

9   Determine the general two-port parameters A,B,C,D for the symmetrical lattice of pure-reactance elements shown in Fig. 3.13 where $Z_1 = X_a$ and $Z_2 = X_b$ with $X_b > X_a$. Hence, verify that $AD - BC = 1$.

10 Obtain the scattering matrices of the two-port networks below:
   (a) a uniform lossless transmission line of length 1 and phase-change coefficient β;
   (b) an ideal transformer of turns ratio $2:1$ and defined by $V_i/V_o = 2$, $I_i/I_o = -1/2$ where V_i, I_i and V_o, I_o are the input and output voltages and currents.

11 Design a second-order low-pass Chebyshev filter with the specification $\varepsilon = 0.67$, $\omega_c = 1\,\text{rad/s}$ and $R_L = 1\,\Omega$. Hence, obtain the circuit components if $\omega_c = 10^4\,\text{rad/s}$ and $R_L = 1.0\,\text{k}\Omega$. The generator impedance is equal to R_L in both cases.

12 Design a high-pass elliptic function π-filter which has less than $1\,\text{dB}$ attenuation at $1\,\text{kHz}$ and more than $30\,\text{dB}$ attenuation at $400\,\text{Hz}$. The filter is used between generator and load impedances of $1\,\Omega$.

13 Define the following terms relating to an operational amplifier: input offset current, input offset voltage, output offset voltage, slew rate.

Estimate V_o for the circuit of Fig. P.1 in which the operational amplifier has an open-circuit voltage gain $A_v = 10^5$, an input resistance $R_i = 1\,\text{M}\Omega$ and an offset voltage $v_i = 2\,\text{mV}$. (C.E.I.)

14 The differential amplifier in Fig. P.2 has a transfer function of the form $V_o = A(V_2 - V_1)$, and has infinite input and zero output impedance.
   (a) Develop an expression for the overall transfer function $[V_o/E](s)$ as $A \to \infty$.
   (b) Calculate the poles of the transfer function for $R_1 = R_2 = 1\,\text{k}\Omega$, $C_1 = 1.0\,\mu\text{F}$ and $C_2 = 0.1\,\mu\text{F}$, and indicate their position in the complex plane. (C.E.I.)

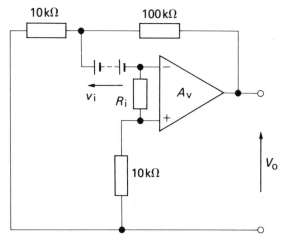

Fig. P.1

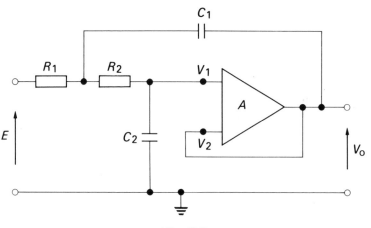

Fig. P.2

15 The filter shown in Fig. 5.11 contains an ideal operational amplifier K of infinite gain, and of infinite input and zero output impedance. Obtain an expression for the overall transfer function $[V_o/V_i](s)$. Given that $C_1 = C_2 = 0{\cdot}1\,\mu\text{F}$, $R_1 = R_2 = 1\,\text{k}\Omega$ and the resonant frequency of the filter is 1 kΩ, calculate the zero-frequency voltage gain of the network. (C.E.I.)

16 Define the following terms relating to an operational amplifier: input offset current, input offset voltage, output offset voltage. How can the effects of these offsets be minimised?

Calculate the voltage gain and input impedance of the amplifier shown in Fig. P.3. The operational amplifier has an open-circuit gain $A = 10^5$, $R_c = 25\ \text{M}\Omega$, $R_i = 100\ \text{k}\Omega$, $R_1 = 2\ \text{k}\Omega$, $R_2 = 100\ \text{k}\Omega$.

(C.E.I.)

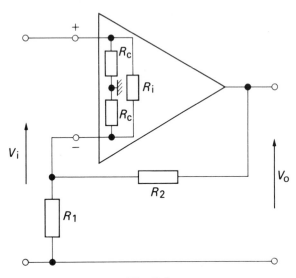

Fig. P.3

17 Determine the inverse z-transform of

(a) $X(z) = \dfrac{(z+5)}{(z-0\cdot5)}$

(b) $X(z) = \dfrac{4z^2}{(z-1)(4z-1)}$

18 By means of the bilinear z-transform, obtain the transfer function $H(z)$ of a digital filter which is equivalent to a second-order Butterworth low-pass filter. The cut-off frequency of the digital filter is 150 Hz and the sampling frequency is 1 kHz.

19 The transfer function $H(s)$ of a filter network is given by

$$H(s) = \frac{(s+1)}{(s^2+5s+6)}$$

Obtain the corresponding expression for $H(z)$ by using the impulse invariant method. The sampling period is 1 second.

20 A low-pass second-order Butterworth digital filter has a cut-off frequency of 100 Hz and a sampling period $T = 1$ ms. Obtain the transfer function $H(s)$ of the corresponding high-pass filter. Hence, by using the substitution $s = k\left[(z-1)/(z+1)\right]$ where $k = 2/T$, obtain an expression for the transfer function $H(z)$ of the digital filter.

21 Design a band-pass FIR filter by the Fourier series method using 11 coefficients and a Hamming window. The filter response is flat over the passband defined by $80 \leqslant f \leqslant 160$ Hz. If the sampling frequency is 800 Hz, obtain an expression for the transfer function $H(z)$ of the digital filter.

Answers

1 2·24, 133 pF
2 $L_0 = 0·1$ mH, $L_1 = 0·3$ mH, $C_1 = 0·0033\,\mu$F
3 $C_0 = 0·026\,\mu$F, $L_2 = 9·1\,\mu$H, $C_2 = 0·001\,\mu$F
4 $L_1 = 2$ H, $C_2 = 1/4$ F, $L_3 = 8$ H, $C_4 = 1/12$ F
5 $\alpha = 2$, $\omega_0 = 1/2RC$
6 Equation (b)
7 $R_a = 150\,\Omega$, $R_b = 200\,\Omega$, $R_c = 600\,\Omega$. Image impedances are $474\,\Omega$ and $506\,\Omega$. Insertion loss is 6·47 dB.

8 $Z_0 = \sqrt{X_a X_b}$, $\gamma = 2\tanh^{-1}\sqrt{\dfrac{X_a}{X_b}}$

9 $A = \dfrac{(X_a + X_b)}{(X_b - X_a)}$ $\qquad B = \dfrac{2X_a X_b}{(X_b - X_a)}$

   $C = \dfrac{2}{(X_b - X_a)}$ $\qquad D = \dfrac{(X_a + X_b)}{(X_b - X_a)}$

10 (a) $[S] = \begin{bmatrix} 0 & e^{-j\beta l} \\ e^{-j\beta l} & 0 \end{bmatrix}$

    (b) $[S] = \dfrac{1}{5}\begin{bmatrix} 3 & 4 \\ 4 & -3 \end{bmatrix}$

11 $L_1 = 0·1$ H, $C_2 = 0·11\,\mu$F
12 Shunt arms: $L_1 = L_3 = 0·676$ H. Series arms: $L_2 = 6·579$ H and $C_2 = 1·025$ F
13 20 mV
14 $(-1 + j3)10^3$
15 $K = 2·37$
16 51, 196 MΩ
17 (a) $x(n) = 11(1/2)^n - 10\delta(n)$

    (b) $x(n) = \dfrac{4}{3}[1 - (1/4)^{n+1}]$

18 $H(z) = \dfrac{z^2 + 2z + 1}{7·627z^2 - 5·704z + 2·077}$

19   $H(z) = \dfrac{1 - 0.2208z^{-1}}{1 - 0.1851z^{-1} + 0.0067z^{-2}}$

20   $H(z) = \dfrac{z^2 - 2z + 1}{1.565z^2 - 1.789z + 0.6462}$

21   $H(z) = -0.02057z^{-1} - 0.07433z^{-2} - 0.03943z^{-3}$
$\qquad\qquad + 0.10553z^{-4} + 0.2z^{-5} + 0.10553z^{-6}$
$\qquad\qquad - 0.03943z^{-7} - 0.07433z^{-8} - 0.02057z^{-9}$

References

1   BOYLE, W. S. and SMITH, G. E. Charge-coupled Semiconductor Devices. *Bell System Technical Journal*, **49**, 587–93, April 1970.
2   MAVOR, J. Signal Processing Applications of CCDs. *The Radio and Electronic Engineer*, **46**, 412–20, August/September 1976.
3   HOLLAND, M. G. and CLAIBORNE, L. T. Practical SAW Devices. *Proceedings IEEE*, **62**, 582–611, May 1974.
4   BRODERSEN, R. W. and WHITE, R. M. CCD and SAW Signal Processing Techniques. *Advances in Electronics and Electron Physics*, **51**, 265, 1980.
5   LAM, H. Y. F. *Analog and Digital Filters*. Prentice-Hall (1979).
6   VAN VALKENBURG, M. E. *Analog Filter Design*. Holt, Rinehart and Winston (1982).
7   KALMAN, R. E. A New Approach to Linear Filtering and Prediction Problems. *Journal Basic Engineering*, **82D**, 35–45, March 1960.
8   KALMAN, R. E. and BUCY, R. S. New Results in Linear Filtering and Prediction Theory. *Journal Basic Engineering*, **83D**, 95–108, 1961.
9   SCHWARTZ, M. and SHAW, L. *Signal Processing*, Chapter 7. McGraw-Hill (1975).
10 TRUNK, G. V. Radar Signal Processing. *Advances in Electronics and Electron Physics*, **45**, 238, 1978.
11 FOSTER, R. M. A Reactance Theorem. *Bell System Technical Journal*, 3-2, 259–67, April 1924.
12 BUDAK, A. *Passive and Active Network Analysis and Synthesis*, Chapter 4. Houghton Mifflin (1974).
13 CAUER, W. The Realisation of Impedances with Prescribed Frequency Dependence. *Archiv fur Electrotechnic*, **15**, 355–8, 1926.
14 CAUER, W. *Synthesis of Linear Communication Networks*. McGraw-Hill (1958).
15 WEINBERG, L. *Network Analysis and Synthesis*. Huntingdon (1975).
16 AATRE, V. K. *Network Theory and Filter Design*. Wiley Eastern (1980).
17 WILLIAMS, A. B. *Electronic Filter Design Handbook*. McGraw-Hill (1981).
18 GIACOLETTO, L. J. *Electronic Designer's Handbook*, Section 5. McGraw-Hill (1977).
19 FINK, D. G. and CHRISTIANSEN, D. *Electronics Engineers Handbook*, Chapter 3. McGraw-Hill (1982).
20 BAILEY, A. E. (ed.) *Microwave Measurement*, Chapter 2. Peter Peregrinus (1985).
21 BUDAK, A. *Passive and Active Network Analysis and Synthesis*, Chapter 17. Houghton Mifflin (1974).
22 BUTTERWORTH, S. On the Theory of Filter Amplifiers. *Wireless Engineer*, **7**, 536–41, October 1930.
23 DARLINGTON, S. Synthesis of Reactive 4-poles which produce Prescribed Insertion Loss Characteristics. *Journal of Mathematics and Physics*, **18**, 257–353, September 1939.
24 LANDON, V. D. Cascade Amplifiers with Maximal Flatness. *RCA Review*, **5**, 34, 1941.

25 STORER, J. E. *Passive Network Synthesis*. McGraw-Hill (1957).
26 GUILLEMIN, E. A. *Synthesis of Passive Networks*. Chapman and Hall (1957).
27 TUTTLE, D. F. *Network Synthesis*, Volume 1. Chapman and Hall (1958).
28 ZVEREV, A. I. *Handbook of Filter Synthesis*. John Wiley (1967).
29 BIRD, G. J. A. *Design of Continuous and Digital Electronic Systems*, Chapter 3. McGraw-Hill (1980).
30 LINVILL, J. G. RC Active Filters, *Proceedings Institute Radio Engineers*, **42**, 555–64, March 1954.
31 SALLEN, R. P. and KEY, E. L. A Practical Method of Designing RC Active Filters. *Transactions Institute Radio Engineers*, **CT-2**, 74–85, 1955.
32 BOWRON, P. and STEPHENSON, F. W. *Active Filters for Communications and Instrumentation*. McGraw-Hill (1979).
33 SEDRA, A. S. and BRACKETT, P. O. *Filter Theory and Design*. Pitman (1979).
34 TELEGEN, B. D. The Gyrator, A New Electric Network. *Philips Research Report*, **3-2**, 81–101, April 1948.
35 ADAMS, K. M. et al. The Gyrator in Electronic Systems. *Advances in Electronics and Electron Physics*, **37**, 79–179, 1975.
36 ANTINIOU, A. Realization of Gyrators Using Op Amps and Their Use in RC Active Network Synthesis. *Proceedings Institution Electrical Engineers*, **116**, 1838–50, November 1969.
37 STOUT, D. F. and KAUFMAN, M. *Handbook of Operational Amplifier Circuit Design*. McGraw-Hill (1976).
38 VAN VALKENBURG, M. E. *Analog Filter Design*. Holt, Rinehart and Winston (1982).
39 GHAUSI, M. S. and LAKER, K. R. *Modern Filter Design*. Prentice-Hall (1981).
40 TERRELL, T. J. *Introduction to Digital Filters*. Macmillan Press (1980).
41 CHEN, C. T. *One Dimensional Digital Signal Processing*, Chapter 5. Marcel Dekker (1979).
42 BOGNER, R. E. and CONSTANTINIDES, A. G. *Introduction to Digital Filtering*. John Wiley (1975).
43 STANLEY, W. D. *Digital Signal Processing*. Reston (1975).
44 OPPENHEIM, A. V. and SCHAFER, R. W. *Digital Signal Processing*, Chapter 9. Prentice-Hall (1975).
45 JONG, M. T. *Methods of Discrete Signal and System Analysis*. McGraw-Hill (1982).
46 McCLELLAN, J. H. et al. A Computer Program for Designing Optimum FIR Digital Filters. *IEEE Transactions on Audio and Electroacoustics*, **21**, 506, 1973.
47 RABINER, R. et al. The Chirp z-transform Algorithm. *IEEE Transactions on Audio and Electroacoustics*, **17**, 86–92, June 1969.
48 ZOBEL, O. J. Theory and Design of Uniform and Composite Electric Wave Filters, *Bell System Technical Journal*, **2-1**, 1–46, January 1923.
49 *Reference Data for Radio Engineers*, Chapter 7. Howard W. Sams (1977).
50 GIACOLETTO L. J. *Electronics Designers Handbook*, Section 6. McGraw-Hill (1977).

Appendices

Appendix A: CCD and SAW filters

(a) CCD filters

The basic three-phase charge-coupled device (CCD) shown in Fig. A.1 consists of a multiple-gate semiconductor, fabricated on a silicon chip using metal-oxide semiconductor (MOS) integrated circuit technology. Information is stored as a charge packet under a gate electrode and the charge can be moved to another gate electrode by using sequential clocking pulses. To transfer the charge from gate ϕ_1 to gate ϕ_2, a positive voltage is applied to ϕ_2 creating a potential well beneath it, while the well under gate ϕ_1 is collapsed by reducing the ϕ_1 voltage. A similar transfer then moves the charge from gate ϕ_2 to gate ϕ_3 and so the device functions as a delay line or shift register.

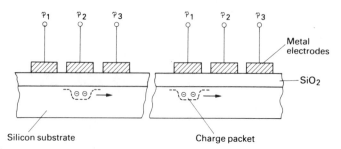

Fig. A.1

The time-delay feature of a CCD enables it to perform a wide range of analogue signal processing functions. Thus, one of its most useful functions is in transversal filtering. In the transversal filter shown in Fig. A.2, the output is a weighted sum of delayed replicas of the input signal. For an N-stage filter, it is necessary to delay and store the last N values of the input signal, then multiply these values by weighted coefficients W_m and finally, sum the products to provide an output which is given by the expression

$$V_o(n) = \sum_{m=1}^{N} W_m V_i(n-m)$$

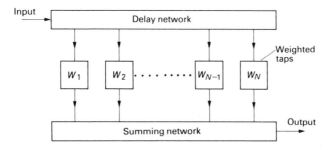

Fig. A.2

where $V_o(n)$ and $V_i(n-m)$ are the nth and $(n-m)$th time samples of the output and input signals respectively. A discrete Fourier transformation then yields the transfer function of the finite impulse response (FIR) transversal filter as

$$H(\omega) = \sum_{m=1}^{N} W_m e^{-j\omega m T_s}$$

where T_s is the sampling period.

The frequency response of this filter has a periodicity equal to the sampling rate and so the input signal must be band-limited to avoid spurious responses due to aliasing effects. Furthermore, the design problem for determining the optimum set of coefficients to provide the closest approximation to a desired frequency response has been solved by using computer programs[46] which perform the task very efficiently.

Extensive work has been done on various techniques for implementing a transversal filter using charge-coupled devices. Usually, the highest performance has been obtained with the split-electrode design shown in Fig. A.3, because it provides an easy method to implement the multiply and add functions required in such filters.

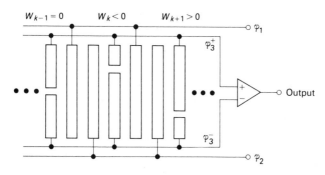

Fig. A.3

In Fig. A.3, the signal charges are sensed on the ϕ_3 electrodes which are unclocked. As the charge transfers from the ϕ_2 electrode to the sensing electrodes (ϕ_3^+ and ϕ_3^-), the current that flows into the sensing line consists of a part that would flow if no signal charge were present, plus a part approximately equal to the signal charge. Thus, the signal charge can be determined by integrating the current flowing to the ϕ_3 electrodes during charge transfer. Weighting is performed by splitting the ϕ_3 electrode and integrating separately the current flowing to each portion. A weighting coefficient of zero corresponds to a split in the centre of the electrode, while positive and negative weightings are achieved by approximately dividing the charge between ϕ_3^+ and ϕ_3^-. The summation is achieved by connecting together the ϕ_3^+ electrodes and the ϕ_3^- electrodes as shown in Fig. A.3. The filter output is obtained by adding and subtracting the ϕ_3^+ and ϕ_3^- line currents in a differential amplifier.

An important limitation of the accuracy of the frequency response of CCD transversal filters is due to errors in the values of the weighting coefficients. As these errors are in general random, they result in an unfiltered portion of the input signal appearing in the output. This result sets a lower limit on the stop-band rejection of the filter and it also adds a ripple to the pass band region.

From a practical point of view, the upper limit of CCDs is about 10 MHz and the potential 'time-delay × bandwidth' products achievable with CCDs is about 1000. Furthermore, to reduce costs, electronically programmable filters are being developed with general signal processing applications. Thus, there are many applications for CCDs in the sonar, radar and communication fields. For example, spectral analysis, using the chirp z-transform (CZT) algorithm[47] is expected to be very useful in image processing, speech recognition and Doppler radar processing.

(b)   SAW filters

In surface acoustic wave filters, ultrasonic waves travel along the surface of a solid and produce minute motions of the particles of the solid. If the solid is a piezoelectric crystal of quartz, a travelling electric field accompanies the acoustic wave and transducers evaporated on to the surface of the solid by lithographic techniques, can couple to the field to provide an electrical output. These SAW devices include delay lines, band pass filters and pulse compression filters.

A SAW delay line filter mounted on a substrate is shown in Fig. A.4. The signal is applied to the transducer on the left and it propagates surface waves in both directions. The wave to the left is absorbed in suitable material, while the wave to the right propagates towards the output transducer and provides an electrical output across the load. Optimum electro-acoustic coupling is obtained when the transducer electrodes are spaced half a wavelength apart for the propagating acoustic signal. The transducer design determines the impulse response of the filter and the

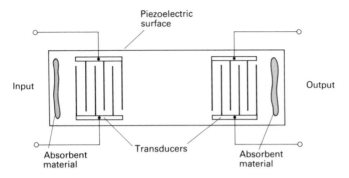

Fig. A.4

frequency of operation is determined by the periodicity of the electrode fingers.

In SAW filters, the transducers are part of a transversal filter as delay is provided by the wave propagation along the substrate and the electrodes tap off and sum the amount of energy at the output of the filter. The magnitude and phasing of this energy can be adjusted by varying the amount of overlap of the fingers and their spacing respectively.

SAW transversal filter designs are based on numerical analyses and resemble the design of finite impulse response (FIR) filters. Design of the tap weighting to achieve an electrode geometry may be carried out with the use of computer programs that model first-order SAW effects as well as second-order effects which can be due to diffraction.

The most useful application of SAW filters has been in pulse compression radars. For example, a reflected signal from a very distant target may be lost in noise because of the limited amount of *peak* power transmitted. The problem may be overcome by transmitting a long duration pulse which varies linearly in frequency from a low value to a high value. This 'chirp' waveform on reception is compressed in time by a SAW filter which is matched to the characteristic of the waveform.

In the pulse compression filter shown in Fig. A.5, the received echo signal is applied to a broad band input transducer with equally spaced electrode fingers. The output transducer has closely spaced fingers, followed by widely spaced fingers. This causes the low frequency energy (which was transmitted first) to be delayed with respect to the high frequency energy (which was transmitted later). Thus, the long duration pulse is compressed into a very short, high amplitude pulse as shown in Fig. A.5. This results in a considerable signal-to-noise improvement and the target can be detected in spite of the interfering noise. However, the pulse compression creates near-in 'time sidelobes' which may be confused with other nearby targets. The time sidelobes are only 13 dB down on the centre peak and can be reduced

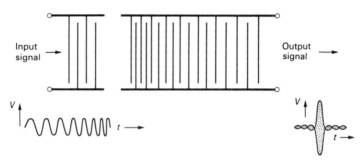

Fig. A.5

by using Taylor amplitude weighting on reception or non-linear FM on transmission.

Another form of dispersive SAW filter used in pulse compression radar is shown in Fig. A.6, where the reflective array compressor (RAC) employing ion-etched grooves in a crystal is illustrated. High-frequency signals are reflected at the shallow, closely spaced grooves nearest the input and output transducers before the lower-frequency components, which are reflected further along the device. The metal film on the piezoelectric lithium niobate substrate allows for the making of fine adjustments in the delay time for different frequency components. With such RAC devices it is possible to achieve large time-bandwidth products about 10 000 and also with large processing gains. The time-bandwidth product which depicts the performance of the device is given by the product of the time duration of a signal and the bandwidth occupied by the signal.

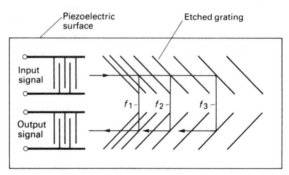

Fig. A.6

In general, SAW filters are smaller than conventional filters made with inductors and capacitors. Centre frequencies of SAW band pass filters have ranged from around 10 MHz to about 1·5 GHz. Most frequencies fall within the range 40–300 MHz and typical bandwidths are from 1–30 MHz.

However, SAW filters have considerable insertion losses ranging from at least 10 dB to as much as 35 dB.

Appendix B: Twin-T network

In the twin-T network shown in Fig. B.1(a), let I_a and I_b be the currents flowing into the output load R_o, for a finite input voltage V_i and a corresponding output voltage V_o. For zero transmission through the network at a specific frequency ω_o we must have

$$V_o = 0$$

and

$$(I_a + I_b) = 0$$

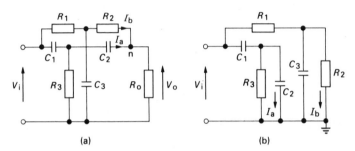

Fig. B.1

Thus, node n is at earth potential and the output load resistor R_o can be short-circuited. This now yields the equivalent circuit shown in Fig. B.1(b), where R_3 and C_2 are in parallel and similarly, C_3 and R_2 are in parallel. Thus, we have

$$(I_a + I_b) = 0$$

or

$$I_a = -I_b$$

Now

$$I_a = \frac{R_3}{(R_3 + 1/j\omega_oC_2)} \times \frac{V_i}{\left[\dfrac{1}{j\omega_oC_1} + \dfrac{R_3(1/j\omega_oC_2)}{(R_3 + 1/j\omega_oC_2)}\right]}$$

or

$$I_a = -\frac{\omega_o^2 R_3 C_1 C_2 V_i}{1 + j\omega_o R_3 (C_1 + C_2)}$$

and

$$I_b = \frac{1/j\omega_oC_3}{(R_2 + 1/j\omega_oC_3)} \times \frac{V_i}{\left[R_1 + \dfrac{R_2(1/j\omega_oC_3)}{(R_2 + 1/j\omega_oC_3)}\right]}$$

or
$$I_b = \frac{V_i}{(R_1 + R_2) + j\omega_o R_1 R_2 C_3}$$

Hence

$$\frac{-\omega_o^2 R_3 C_1 C_2 V_i}{1 + j\omega_o R_3 (C_1 + C_2)} = \frac{-V_i}{(R_1 + R_2) + j\omega_o R_1 R_2 C_3}$$

or

$$\omega_o^2 R_3 C_1 C_2 (R_1 + R_2) + j\omega_o^3 (R_3 C_1 C_2 R_1 R_2 C_3) = 1 + j\omega_o R_3 (C_1 + C_2)$$

Equating real and imaginary parts on both sides yields

$$\omega_o^2 R_3 C_1 C_2 (R_1 + R_2) = 1$$

or
$$\omega_o^2 = \frac{1}{C_1 C_2 R_3 (R_1 + R_2)}$$

and

$$\omega_o^3 (R_3 C_1 C_2 R_1 R_2 C_3) = \omega_o R_3 (C_1 + C_2)$$

or
$$\omega_o^2 = \frac{(C_1 + C_2)}{R_1 R_2 C_1 C_2 C_3}$$

Appendix C: Prototype filters[48-50]

In the older classical theory, basic filter structures, from which other more sophisticated structures could be built, were called *prototype filters*. The procedure was to take a filter structure, analyse it, and then obtain as much information as possible about its characteristics. In order to do this easily, ideal components were assumed by considering them to be pure reactances. The procedure led to a great simplification in the theory, which would otherwise have been very cumbersome. Moreover, the transition to practical components with resistance was easily made by slight modification of the basic results obtained.

In this so-called 'image-parameter' approach the analysis was either qualitative, involving simple graphical considerations, or it was quantitative, and required a more rigorous mathematical treatment of the filter structure. The starting point was usually a consideration of the input impedance of a correctly terminated filter of T or π configuration. As an example, for a T configuration with pure reactances jX_1 and jX_2 of opposite sign (the signs being included in X_1 and X_2) we have

$$Z_{0T} = \sqrt{Z_1 Z_2 + Z_1^2/4}$$

and
$$Z_{0T} = \sqrt{jX_1 jX_2 - X_1^2/4} = j\sqrt{X_1(X_1/4 + X_2)}$$

for the input impedance of the filter.

For a T-filter terminated in Z_{0T}, this meant that power could only be dissipated in Z_{0T} if it was real and resistive i.e. certain frequencies could pass through the filter which corresponded to the *pass band*. This can be illustrated for a low-pass filter where the low-pass configuration and symbolism are shown in Fig. C.1. The low-pass filter passes all frequencies from zero to a certain cut-off frequency f_c.

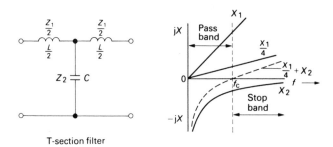

T-section filter

Fig. C.1

For the T-section we have

$$Z_1 = j\omega L \qquad X_1 = \omega L$$

$$Z_2 = -j\,1/\omega C \qquad X_2 = -1/\omega C$$

and

$$\frac{X_1}{4} + X_2 = \frac{\omega L}{4} - \frac{1}{\omega C}$$

A plot of $(X_1/4 + X_2)$ is shown in Fig. C.1. The cut-off frequency f_c occurs when $Z_{0T} = 0$ and the filter behaves as a short-circuit. We then have

$$\frac{\omega_c L}{4} - \frac{1}{\omega_c C} = 0$$

or

$$\omega_c^2 = 4/LC$$

with

$$f_c = 1/\pi\sqrt{LC}$$

which is the cut-off frequency for a T-section filter. Similar considerations also apply to the corresponding π-section configuration.

The low-pass filter considered above is characterised by the fact that $Z_1 Z_2 = L/C$ (a constant) and this constant was usually denoted by k^2. Thus, as $k = \sqrt{L/C}$ was used as the design impedance of the filter, the prototype filter was also known as a constant-k filter. However, two serious drawbacks of the prototype filter were known to be:

(a) the attenuation characteristic increased slowly beyond cut-off, and
(b) the characteristic impedance varied considerably over the pass band and caused a mismatch.

These drawbacks were more or less minimised by using *m*-derived filters where *m* was a numerical factor $(0 < m < 1)$ and the value of *m* determined the property of the *m*-derived filter. Essentially, the component values of the prototype filter were modified by the factor *m* and an additional component had to be used in the shunt arm of the T-configuration in order to maintain the same value of Z_{0T} regardless of the value of *m*. This is illustrated in Fig. C.2.

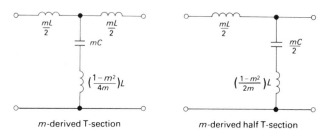

m-derived T-section   m-derived half T-section

Fig. C.2

The second drawback of the prototype filter was minimised by using half of an *m*-derived T-section as illustrated in Fig. C.2. Such half-section filters had a fairly constant value of characteristic impedance over most of the pass band when $m = 0.6$. It was usual to use two such half-sections (one at the input and one at the output) of the overall filter structure and so they were known as terminating half-sections.

Several *m*-derived filters with different values of *m* were often connected in series to form a *composite* filter, since they all had the same characteristic impedance, which was independent of the value of *m*. A typical structure consisted of a prototype filter $(m = 1.0)$ in series with one or two *m*-derived sections employing a value of $m = 0.3$ or $m = 0.4$. Finally, this structure was terminated using a matching half-section with $m = 0.6$ at either end. A typical composite filter structure is shown in Fig. C.3.

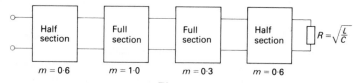

Fig. C.3

Appendix D: Filter tables

Butterworth approximation

The various factors of the *inverse* of the transfer function $H(s)$ for Butterworth low-pass filters of order *n* are tabulated in Table D.1.

Table D.1

n	$1/H(s)$
1	$(s+1)$
2	$(s^2 + 1{\cdot}414s + 1)$
3	$(s+1)(s^2 + s + 1)$
4	$(s^2 + 0{\cdot}765s + 1)(s^2 + 1{\cdot}848s + 1)$
5	$(s+1)(s^2 + 0{\cdot}618s + 1)(s^2 + 1{\cdot}618s + 1)$
6	$(s^2 + 0{\cdot}518s + 1)(s^2 + 1{\cdot}414s + 1)(s^2 + 1{\cdot}932s + 1)$
7	$(s+1)(s^2 + 0{\cdot}44s + 1)(s^2 + 1{\cdot}247s + 1)(s^2 + 1{\cdot}802s + 1)$
8	$(s^2 + 0{\cdot}39s + 1)(s^2 + 1{\cdot}111s + 1)(s^2 + 1{\cdot}166s + 1)(s^2 + 1{\cdot}962s + 1)$

Chebyshev approximation

Various values of the Chebyshev polynomial $C_n(\omega)$ for low-pass filters of order n are tabulated in Table D.2.

Table D.2

n	$C_n(\omega)$
1	ω
2	$2\omega^2 - 1$
3	$4\omega^3 - 3\omega$
4	$8\omega^4 - 8\omega^2 + 1$
5	$16\omega^5 - 20\omega^3 + 5\omega$
6	$32\omega^6 - 48\omega^4 + 18\omega^2 - 1$
7	$64\omega^7 - 112\omega^5 + 56\omega^3 - 7\omega$
8	$128\omega^8 - 256\omega^6 + 160\omega^4 - 32\omega^2 + 1$

Elliptic function filters

The relevant parameters ω_s, A_1, A_2 and the normalised component values for third-order and fifth-order low-pass filters with the configuration shown in Fig. D.1 are tabulated in Tables D.3 and D.4 respectively. The capacitance values are in farads and the inductance values are in henrys. The parameter A_2 is in dB.

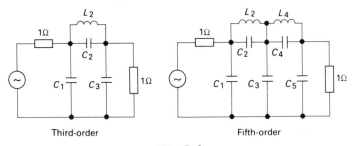

Fig. D.1

Table D.3

ω_s	A_2	C_1	L_2	C_2	C_3
1·756	20	0·850	0·871	0·290	0·850
2·082	25	0·902	0·951	0·188	0·902
2·465	30	0·941	1·012	0·125	0·941
2·921	35	0·958	1·057	0·084	0·958
3·542	40	0·988	1·081	0·057	0·988

(a) $A_1 = 0\cdot1$ dB

ω_s	A_2	C_1	L_2	C_2	C_3
1·416	20	1·267	0·748	0·536	1·267
1·636	25	1·361	0·853	0·344	1·361
1·935	30	1·425	0·924	0·226	1·425
2·283	35	1·479	0·976	0·152	1·479
2·713	40	1·514	1·015	0·102	1·514

(b) $A_1 = 0\cdot5$ dB

ω_s	A_2	C_1	L_2	C_2	C_3
1·295	20	1·570	0·613	0·805	1·570
1·484	25	1·688	0·729	0·497	1·688
1·732	30	1·783	0·812	0·322	1·783
2·048	35	1·852	0·865	0·214	1·852
2·418	40	1·910	0·905	0·145	1·910
2·816	45	1·965	0·929	0·101	1·965

(c) $A_1 = 1\cdot0$ dB

Table D.4

ω_s	A_2	C_1	L_2	C_2	C_3	L_4	C_4	C_5
1·309	35	0·977	1·139	0·230	1·488	0·740	0·742	0·701
1·414	40	1·010	1·193	0·177	1·586	0·875	0·530	0·766
1·540	45	1·032	1·228	0·140	1·657	0·968	0·401	0·836
1·690	50	1·044	1·180	0·118	1·726	1·134	0·283	0·885
1·860	55	1·072	1·275	0·088	1·761	1·100	0·241	0·943
2·048	60	1·095	1·292	0·070	1·801	1·148	0·192	0·988
2·262	65	1·108	1·308	0·056	1·834	1·191	0·151	1·022
2·512	70	1·112	1·319	0·044	1·858	1·225	0·119	1·044

(a) $A_1 = 0.1$ dB

ω_s	A_2	C_1	L_2	C_2	C_3	L_4	C_4	C_5
1·186	35	1·439	0·967	0·358	1·762	0·600	1·116	1·026
1·270	40	1·495	1·016	0·279	1·880	0·696	0·840	1·114
1·369	45	1·530	1·063	0·218	1·997	0·795	0·627	1·241
1·481	50	1·563	1·099	0·172	2·113	0·875	0·482	1·320
1·618	55	1·559	1·140	0·134	2·188	0·949	0·369	1·342
1·782	60	1·603	1·143	0·108	2·248	0·995	0·291	1·449
1·963	65	1·626	1·158	0·086	2·306	1·037	0·230	1·501
2·164	70	1·624	1·178	0·068	2·319	1·078	0·182	1·521

(b) $A_1 = 0.5$ dB

Table D.4 *(Contd)*

ω_s	A_2	C_1	L_2	C_2	C_3	L_4	C_4	C_5
1·145	35	1·783	0·827	0·474	1·978	0·488	1·487	1·276
1·217	40	1·861	0·873	0·372	2·142	0·578	1·107	1·427
1·245	45	1·923	0·947	0·293	2·296	0·684	0·848	1·553
1·407	50	1·933	0·963	0·223	2·392	0·750	0·626	1·635
1·528	55	1·976	0·986	0·178	2·519	0·811	0·487	1·732
1·674	60	2·007	1·003	0·141	2·620	0·862	0·380	1·807
1·841	65	2·036	1·016	0·113	2·703	0·901	0·301	1·873
2·036	70	2·056	1·028	0·089	2·732	0·934	0·239	1·928

(c) $A_1 = 1 \cdot 0 \, \text{dB}$

Appendix E: Operational amplifiers

The op amp is a high gain differential amplifier which is operated from equal positive and negative supply voltages. Its two input terminals are designated as invert (− sign) and non-invert (+ sign) respectively and it has only one output terminal. The characteristic performance of the op amp is usually specified using the following terminology.

1. *Input impedance*: the impedance measured at one input terminal with the other input terminal grounded.
2. *Input offset voltage*: the voltage across the two input terminals for zero output voltage.
3. *Input offset current*: the difference in the two input currents for zero output voltage.
4. *Input bias current*: the average value of the two input currents for zero output voltage.
5. *Output impedance*: the impedance measured at the output terminal without feedback.
6. *Output voltage swing*: the maximum range of the output voltage excursion.
7. *Supply voltage rejection ratio*: the change in the output voltage for unit voltage change in the supply voltage, with both inputs short-circuited.
8. *Common-mode rejection ratio*: the ratio of the gain with a differential signal at the input, to the gain with an equal signal at each input.
9. *Open-loop gain*: the low-frequency voltage gain without feedback.
10. *Slew rate*: the maximum rate of change of the output voltage for a step input voltage.
11. *Bandwidth (open-loop)*: the frequency range from d.c. to the unity gain frequency.

Typical values of various parameters for a general-purpose op amp like the μA 741 (Fairchild) are shown in Table E.1. This op amp is used

Table E.1

Parameter	Value (*typical*)
Input impedance	1·0 MΩ
Input offset voltage	1·0 mV
Input offset current	30 nA
Input bias current	200 nA
Output impedance	75 Ω
Output voltage swing	± 14 V
Supply voltage rejection ratio	30 μV/V
Common-mode rejection ratio	90 dB
Open-loop gain	200 000
Slew rate (unity gain)	0·5 V/μs
Bandwidth (open-loop)	10 MHz

extensively in analogue circuits and is available as a single chip integrated circuit in a TO-5 can or as a dual-inline package.

For specific applications, a wide variety of op amps are available. For example, the μA 747 (Fairchild) is a dual version of the μA 741 in a single package, while the CA 3140 (RCA) employs an input FET stage to obtain a very high input impedance of 1·5 TΩ. Finally, commercial op amps such as the μA 741C operate with supply voltages of $\pm$ 18 V, but other op amps such as the LH 0003 (National Semiconductors) use supply voltages as high as $\pm$ 40 V.

Index